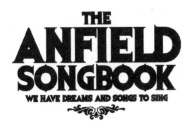

THE ANFIELD SONGBOOK

WE HAVE DREAMS AND SONGS TO SING

YOU'LL NEVER WALK ALONE

LIVERPOOL
FOOTBALL CLUB

EST·1892 ®

THE
ANFIELD
SONGBOOK

WE HAVE DREAMS AND SONGS TO SING

Sport Media
A Trinity Mirror Business

Produced by Sport Media, Trinity Mirror North West

Executive Editor: Ken Rogers
Senior Editor: Steve Hanrahan
Senior Production Editor: Paul Dove
Senior Art Editor: Rick Cooke
Sub Editors: Roy Gilfoyle, Adam Oldfield, James Cleary
Designers: Glen Hind, Colin Sumpter, Barry Parker, Lee Ashun,
Alison Gilliland, Jamie Dunmore, James Kenyon, Lisa Critchley
Writers: Chris McLoughlin, John Hynes, Simon Hughes,
William Hughes, Alan Jewell
Sales and Marketing Manager: Elizabeth Morgan
Marketing Executive: Claire Brown
Sales and Marketing Assistant: Karen Cadman

First published in Great Britain in 2010 and reprinted in 2011 by:
Trinity Mirror Sport Media.
PO Box 48, Old Hall Street, Liverpool L69 3EB.
Copyright of Liverpool Football Club and Athletic Grounds Limited,
except where stated.

ISBN: 978-1-906802-44-8

Printed and bound by CPI Group (UK) Ltd, Croydon, CRO 4YY

66 There's not one club in Europe with an anthem like You'll Never Walk Alone. There's not one club in the world so united with the fans. I sat there watching the Liverpool fans and they sent shivers down my spine. A mass of 40,000 people became one force behind their team. That's something not many teams have. For that I admire Liverpool more than anything 99

— Johan Cruyff

66 The only thing I fear is missing an open goal in front of the Kop. I would die if that were to happen. When they start singing You'll Never Walk Alone my eyes start to water. There have been times when I've actually been crying while I've been playing 99

— **Kevin Keegan**

We're A Happy Band...

 tood shoulder to shoulder, scarves held aloft, the images of Liverpool supporters singing You'll Never Walk Alone before a game at Anfield are some of the most famous in football.

Wherever you are in the world, if you hear that song you think of Liverpool Football Club, of Anfield, of the Kop in full voice.

Rodgers and Hammerstein may have wrote it, and Gerry Marsden took it to number one in the charts, but it is the supporters of Liverpool FC who have made it world famous.

It is Anfield's anthem. The motto on our badge. A Kopite's calling card. A song sung with passion, desire, defiance and emotion.

But You'll Never Walk Alone is far from the only song to pass from the collective lips of Liverpool supporters. It is simply the most famous of hundreds of songs and chants that have passed through the collective lips of Liverpudlians over the years.

That singing culture has played a significant part in creating Anfield's unique aura and making the Kop the most famous stand in football.

Collective chanting and singing at football matches is taken for granted now, but before the early 1960s that wasn't the case.

It all changed at Anfield in 1963/64. With The

Beatles taking the Mersey Sound around the world and Bill Shankly's Liverpool en-route to winning the league, those on the Kop wanted to shout about it.

So they did, en-masse, with up to 28,000 singing and swaying along to whatever was played over the PA System before kick-off.

It was communal karaoke, the like of which had never been seen before in English football, with the natural Scouse wit soon lending itself to adapting the words to well known tunes to express admiration for their heroes and distain for opponents.

And so the sound of Anfield resonated around the world and the Liverpool FC songbook began.

The partisan vocal backing our players have received during the course of our history has been a significant factor in making us English football's most successful club. The Anfield Songbook is a tribute to that magnificent support.

We have compiled hundreds of songs and chants that have been written and sung by Liverpool supporters over the years – although there are several we simply can't publish!

Many have been aired at Anfield, others only on away trips. Some have never been heard outside pubs and bars, a few have been posted by creative Reds on Liverpool FC message boards.

Our collection is not definitive – no LFC songbook ever could be – and the words to certain tunes have varied, been changed and updated over the years, but The Anfield Songbook gives a taste of the unique, inventive, humourous and inspirational songs that have been sung by Liverpool FC supporters all round the fields of Anfield Road.

You never walk alone when you're a Kopite. You never sing alone either.

66 Forget the Beatles and all the rest. This is the real Liverpool sound. It's real singing, and it's what the Kop is all about 99

— **Bill Shankly**

*The songs in this book are those sung
by the supporters of Liverpool FC and do
not necessarily represent the position of
Liverpool Football Club*

A Little Touch Of Scotland

A little touch of Scotland came to
Liverpool one day,
He looked around and said: "Och man aye,
this is where I'll stay,"
And from that moment he worked hard
to build a team so grand,
And now today we have the greatest
team in all the land.

[Chorus]:
Shankly, oh yes Bill Shankly,
Shankly we love you.
For all the things you've done for us
while here at Liverpool,
Bill Shankly we thank you.

Nowhere would you find a man who is the
same as he,
And all who meet him love him for his humility.
For that and many other things our thanks we
give to him,
And do you see we're talking of Bill Shankly,
Aye that's him!

Shankly, oh yes Bill Shankly,
Shankly we love you.
For all the things you've done for us
while here at Liverpool,
Bill Shankly we thank you.

A Liverpool Fan

(To the tune 'Bachelor Boy' by Cliff Richard)

When I was young, my father said:
"Son I have something to say,"
And what he told me I'll never forget,
Until my dyin' day.
He said:

[Chorus]:
Son you are a Liverpool fan,
And that's the way to stay, ay-ay,
Happy to be a Liverpool fan,
Until your dyin' day.

So off to Anfield we would go,
And we'd stand in the Kop.
We'd cheer on the Mighty Reds,
As they climbed to the top.

Son you are a Liverpool fan,
And that's the way to stay, ay-ay,
Happy to be a Liverpool fan,
Until your dyin' day.

When I got older,
Me and me Dad,
In Europe we'd stand up.
And we'd watch our LFC,
Win the European Cup.

Son you are a Liverpool fan,
And that's the way to stay, ay-ay,
Happy to be a Liverpool fan,
Until your dyin' day.

A Red For Evermore

(To the tune of 'It Doesn't Matter Anymore' by Buddy Holly)

This is my story, boys, and it's no lie,
Gonna be a Scouser, 'til the day I die,
Stevie G, what have you done to me?
Well I'll guess I'll be a Red for evermore.

Do you remember, Kopites, that December,
When Shankly came, we used to sing his name.
Well whoops-a-daisy, then along came Paisley,
And I'll guess I'll be a Red for evermore.

There's no other sight, like Rushie scoring,
No other sound, like Kopites roaring,
"We're Liverpool FC,"
"We all hate Chel-sea,"
"And Man yooooooooooooo."

A-B-L-E-T-T

A-B-L *[clap clap]*,
E-T-T *[clap clap]*,
Gary Ablett is the one for me.

*(Originally the song for Albert Stubbins, this was revived for
Gary Ablett in the 1980s but got its best airing of all at Villa
Park in 1994 when news filtered through from Goodison Park
that Ablett, then playing for Everton, had scored an own goal
against Wimbledon that looked to be sending the Blues down)*

After The Ball Is Over

After the game is over,
After the whistle blew,
Campbell got excited,
And down the wing he flew.
He passed the ball to Liddell,
Liddell scored a goal,
And left poor Everton's goalie,
Flying on his 'ole.

Agger Doo
(To the tune 'Agadoo' by Black Lace)

Agger doo, doo, doo,
Plays with Carra or Sami,
Agger doo, doo, doo,
Plays for Liverpool FC.

He can shoot,
He can score,
From thirty yards like Stevie G.
Agger doo, doo, doo,
Plays for Liverpool FC.

Agger doo, doo, doo,
Since we singed him from Brondby,
Agger doo, doo, doo,
Plays for Liverpool FC.

To the left,
To the right,
He brings strikers to their knees.
Agger doo, doo, doo,
Plays for Liverpool FC.

A-L-B-E-R-T

You can keep Billy Liddell,
You can keep Roger Hunt,
David Johnson was a bit of a ****.
You can keep Kenny Dalglish,
You can keep Ian Rush,
Albert Stubbins is the man for us.
[Chorus]:
A-L-B [clap clap],
E-R-T [clap clap],
Albert Stubbins is the one for me.

*(One of the earliest player songs in honour of an Anfield
goalscoring legend, although not aired until
after his retirement)*

Allez Allez

Allez allez, (Allez allez),
Allez allez, (Allez allez), Gerard Houllier,
Allez allez, (Allez allez),
Allez allez, (Allez allez), Gerard Houllier.

(A popular chant during the reign of the Frenchman and can be traced back to Boavista in 2001, where 500 travelling Reds started the tune during half-time of the Champions League tie. It has since spawned variations including: 'Allez Allez, how good does Stevie play?')

A-L-O-N-S-0

(To the tune of The Beatles' 'Ob-La-Di Ob-La-Da')

[Chorus]:
A-L-O-N-S-O, it's Alonso, Xabi, Xabi Alonso,
A-L-O-N-S-O, it's Alonso, Xabi, Xabi Alonso.

He came from Sociedad to play in our midfield,
His passing and his shooting are sublime,
If we had to choose between him and Fat Frank,
We would choose Xabi every time.

A-L-O-N-S-O, it's Alonso, Xabi, Xabi Alonso,
A-L-O-N-S-O, it's Alonso, Xabi, Xabi Alonso.

We drew Luton Town in the FA Cup,
Xabi and the keeper had a race,
Xabi had a shot from 70 yards,
You should have seen the look on Gerrard's face.

A-L-O-N-S-O, it's Alonso, Xabi, Xabi Alonso,
A-L-O-N-S-O, it's Alonso, Xabi, Xabi Alonso.

Alonso, Alonso, Alonso (I)

(To the tune of 'Let It Snow')

Oh, he is a midfield maestro,
And his passing's so delightful,
Everyone wants to know,
Alonso, Alonso, Alonso.

Alonso, Alonso, Alonso (II)

(To the tune 'Mexican Hat')

Alonso, Alonso, Alonso,
Alonso, Alonso, Alonso,
Alonso, Alonso, Alonso,
Alonso, Alonso, Alonso!

(This was sung at a fast pace while jumping at the same time)

And Here's To You

(To the tune of Simon and Garfunkel's 'Mrs Robinson')

And here's to you, Slovan Liberec,
Liverpool loves you more than you will know *(wo, wo, wo)*.
God bless you please Torpedo Moscow.
Liverpool holds a place for those we play,
(Hey, hey, hey, . . . hey, hey, hey).

We'd like to know CSKA or even Feyenoord,
We'd like to help them drink the night away.

Look around and all you'd see were banners made of red.
The famous Kopites singing off their heads.

And here's to you Girondins Bordeaux,
Bottles of red just a pound a throw *(wo, wo, wo)*.
God bless you, please Zurich Grasshoppers.
Expensive but the girls are worth the pay,
(Hey, hey, hey, . . . hey, hey, hey).

Play it in a country east where no-one ever goes.
Play it at Dukla Prague's little ground.
Skonta Riga, Copenhagen, Honved or Liege.
Those teams now never come around.

Allez allez les vertes St Etienne,
Moenchengladbach, Bruges we so miss you *(you, hoo, hoo)*.
Where are you now Polands' Widzew Lodz.
It's teams like you we really want to play.
(Allez, Allez, Allez, Allez).

Sitting on the sofa on a Friday afternoon,
Watching the Champions League draw come on through.
Barca, Porto, Bayern, Mancs, the same teams once again,
Ev'ry way you look at it, the fans still lose.

Where have you gone, Dynamo Dresden?
A Kopite turns his jaded eyes to you *(you, hoo, hoo)*.
What's that you say, Lennart Johannson,
UEFA have swept the likes of Dresden away?
(Please don't say, please don't say).

*(This song was written in 2004 in homage to the UEFA Cup
by a Kopite called Stephen Davies (aka 'Rushian)'
and posted on various Internet forums.)*

Anfield

(To the hymn 'Jerusalem' by Hubert Parry)

And did Shankly in ancient times,
Walk upon Anfield's pastures green,
And was our holy manager God,
To Europe's greatest football team.

And did Paisley surpass him still,
And bring back titles and cups at will,
And was the Spion Kop builded here,
Beneath the Liverbird's bill.

Bring me Fagan and Tommy Smith,
Bring me Benitez's Spanish fire,
Bring me Gerrard! and Carragher!
The backbone of our team tonight.

We will not cease from mental fight,
Nor shall our swords sleep in our hands.
'Til we have won the cup for good,
And brought it back to Anfield again.

[Alternative version entitled 'Stanley Park']:

And did those feet in Shankly's time,
Walk upon Anfield's pastures green,
And was Fowler, the lamb of God,
On Anfield's pleasant pastures seen.

And was the soul of Bob divine,
Shine forth upon our future days,
And was our Anfield builded there,
Among those dark and manic roads.

Bring me my cup (my cup) of burning gold,
Bring me my trophies of desire,
Bring me my spears o'clouds unfold,
Bring me Johnny's ring of fire.

I will not cease my groundshare fight,
Nor shall my (my) scarf sleep in hand,
'Til we have built Stanley Park,
In Anfield's green and pleasant land.

Liverpool,
Liverpool,
Liverpool.

(Although the music was written by Sir Hubert Parry in 1916, the words came about from a short poem by William Blake in the early nineteenth century. Neither version of this song has ever been sung at a Liverpool match but both would sound good if they were!)

Anfield Rap

The official club anthem for the 1988 FA
Cup final meeting with Wimbledon was
Craig Johnston's idea, not John Barnes'
as many think, and is a parody of a
number of hip hop tracks. At the time,
there were only two Scousers in the first
team – John Aldridge and Steve
McMahon – and the theme of the song
evolves around their team-mates'
strange accents. The song made it to
number three in the UK charts, while the
accompanying video has ensured it will
live long in our memories.

Anfield Rap
(Red Machine In Full Effect)

Liverpool FC is hard as hell,
United, Tottenham, Arsenal.
Watch my lips, and I will spell,
'Cause they don't just play, but they can rap
aswell.

Liverpool FC,
Liverpool FC.

(My idea was to build Liverpool into a bastion
of invincibility... aah...aah...ahh...aah ...had
Napoleon had that idea he'd have conquered
the bloody world)

[Chorus]:
Walk on...walk on...with hope...in your
heart...and you'll ne...ver walk...alone.

Alright Aldo,
Sound as a pound,
I'm cushty la but there's nothing down.
The rest of the lads ain't got it sussed,
We'll have to learn 'em to talk like us.

Well I'm rapping now, I'm rapping for fun,
I'm your goalie, your number one.
You can take the mick, don't call me a clown,
Any more lip and you're going down.

Ar ay Ace, we're great me and you,

But the other lads don't talk like we do.
No they don't talk like we do, do they do la,
We'll have to learn 'em to talk propah.

*Walk on... walk on... with hope... in your heart...
and you'll ne...ver walk... alone*

You two Scousers are always yapping,
I'm gonna show you some serious rapping.
I come from Jamaica, my name is John Barn-es,
When I do my thing the crowd go bananas.

How's he doing the Jamaica rap?
He's from just south of the Watford Gap.
He gives us stick about the north/south divide,
'Cause they got the jobs,
Yeah, but we got the side.

Well I came to England looking for fame,
So come on Kenny man, give us a game.
'Cause I'm sat on the bench paying my dues with
the blues,
I'm very big down under, but my wife disagrees.

They've won the league, bigger stars than Dallas,
They got more silver than Buckingham Palace.
No-one knows quite what to expect,
When the red machine's in full effect.

Well Steve McMahon sure can rap,
It's about time he had an England cap.
So come on Bobby Robson, he's the man,
'Cause if anyone can, Macca can.
Macca-can... Macca-can... Macca-can... Macca-can...

Liverpool FC is hard as hell.
(My idea was to build Liverpool up and up and
up until eventually they would be untouchable.
Everybody would have to submit.
Give in, give in, give in)

We're Highland lads,
Och-ai the noo,
And there's four of us,
And only two of you.
So if you want nai trouble,
And you don't want a slap,
You'd better teach us the Anfield rap.

Don't forget us paddies,
And me the Great Dane,
And I'm from London mate so watch your game.
Well you two scousers, you're always squawking,
But we'll just let our feet do the talking.

Our lads have come from all over the place,
They talk dead funny, but they play dead great.
Well now we've gotta learn 'em to talk real cool,
The song you've gotta learn if you're Liverpool.

Walk on... walk on... with hope... in your heart...
and you'll ne...ver walk... alone
You'll never walk alone.

Ho-ho my word,
That's unbelievable, it really is.
I think they should stick to playing football.
Terrible. What do you think Kenny?
Oh yeah!

Anfield Way

Down Anfield Way the world is gay,
All Kopites are to tingle,
With rows and rows of crimson flags,
From Bootle up to Dingle.
The toast is to eleven men,
Who wear the scarlet jersey,
Their names will live forever more,
Along the river Mersey.

They'll take their place in history,
Amongst the all-time greats,
Thompson, Byrne, St John, and Hunt,
And Skipper Rowdy Yeats.
So let us sing a song or two,
On Wembley's famous ground,
And let London town re-echo,
To that famous Mersey sound.

They beat the Leeds two goals to one,
And Rowdy met the queen,
And Gerry broke his collar bone,
As brave as you have seen.
And when they bring that cup back home,
Through streets all paved in Red,
Those Liverbirds will fly away,
Just like Bill Shankly said.

(Liverpool's first ever FA Cup winning team is immortalised
in song after their 2-1 Wembley victory over Leeds United
in 1965. The song, along with the joyous scenes which
greeted the team on their return to Merseyside,
suitably reflect the mood of the fans and the
importance of that first FA Cup)

Anfield Wig Walk
(To the tune of 'Tennessee Wig Walk' by Bonnie Lou)

I'm a knock-kneed chicken,
I'm bow-legged hen,
I haven't been so happy,
Since I don't know when.
I walk with a wiggle,
And talk with a squawk,
Doing the Anfield wig walk.

Arbeloa
(To the tune of 'From Me To You by The Beatles)

Arbelo-Arbeloaaaaaaa,
Arbelo-Arbeloaaaaaaa,
If there's anything that you want,
If there's anything he can do,
Just give him the ball and he'll run through and
score a goal for Liverpool.
Arbelo-Arbeloaaaaaaa,
Arbelo-Arbeloaaaaaaa.

Aye-aye Sami
(To the tune of 'She'll Be Coming Round The Mountain')

Singin' aye-aye Sami Hyypia,
Singin' aye-aye Sami Hyypia,
Singin' aye-aye Sami,
Aye-aye Sami,
Aye-aye Sami Hyypia.

Benitez
(Sung To 'The Macarena' by Los del Rio)

He comes from Spain and he doesn't speak good English,
But we don't care 'cos he's gonna make us winners,
The European Cup will be ours before he's finished,
RAFAEL BENITEZ!

Benny Is A Dancer
(To the tune of Snap's 'Rhythm Is A Dancer)

Benny is a dancer,
Skipping past defenders,
Benayoun is everywhere!

*(Sung during the Europa League quarter-final
victory over Benfica in April 2010)*

Best Midfield In The World

(To the tune of 'The Entertainer' by Billy Joel)

Whoa-oh, whoa-oh, whoa-oh,
We've got the best midfield in the world,
Xabi Alonso, Momo Sissoko, Gerrard and
Mascherano-o-oh!

(This song emerged in 2007 when the Reds were on their way to Athens for the Champions League final. It was famously sung in Monastaraki, Athens, by hundreds of Kopites doing a conga on the night after Liverpool had lost the final to AC Milan with two YouTube videos of it receiving over half-a-million hits!)

Big Ron Yeats

Let me tell you of our football team,
Liverpool is the name.
We've won the league, we've won the cup,
We're the finest in the game.
We've got the greatest skipper any manager
could employ,
Let's drink six crates to big Ron Yeats,
Bill Shankly's pride and joy.

(Also known as 'Bill Shankly's Pride And Joy', this song salutes the leadership of Big Rowdy Ron Yeats)

Bill Shankly From Glenbuck

(To the tune of 'Sean South From Garryowen' by the Wolfe Tones)

'Twas on a cold December's day,

Back in 1959,
When a man came down from Huddersfield Town,
To lead the Anfield line.
He bought Yeats from Dundee and St John,
And the football world was shook,
This man he became a legend,
Bill Shankly from Glenbuck.

On the Kop we'd sway and sing,
'Til our hearts would burst with pride,
And Shanks he made a pact with us,
To build another side.
With Keegan, Tosh and Steve Heighway,
The great man kept his word,
Then in '74 he bade farewell,
Our dear old Scottish Laird.

Now when Shanks was gone we sang 'Walk On'
But feared we'd walk alone,
The search was on to find the one,
Who could fill the master's throne.
The one we crowned became renowned,
Throughout the football game,
Three European Cups, six championships,
Bob Paisley was his name.

Now when Bob stepped down he left his crown,
Inside his Anfield home.
Joe Fagan came and brought new fame,
With a treble won in Rome.
Though the Heysel year left Joe in tears,
The following year he'd sing,
When we won the league and FA Cup,
And Kenny was our king.

When he played in red, Bob Paisley said,
He's the best he'd ever seen,
And the team he built in '88,
Ruled the football league supreme.
And when Hillsborough left us all bereaved,
And the Kop bedecked in flowers,
Kenny proved he truly was a king,
In Anfield's darkest hour.

Now the mantle's being past to a man from France,
And it's Houllier we praise,
As the Reds walk on, the Kop's in song,
And we savour glory days.
Days of ball to feet, of victory sweet,
Days of passion, guile and fire,
The legacy of one so great,
Bill Shankly from Ayrshire.

*(Penned by John Mackin, Kop season ticket holder since
1975, long-time fanzine writer, founder member of
Reclaim The Kop and co-author of Redmen: A Season on
The Drink)*

Billy Liddell
*(To the tune of Dean Martin's signature song
'That's Amore')*

When he runs down the wing,
You can hear the Kop sing,
Billy Liddell!
When he runs through to score,
You can hear the Kop roar,
Billy Liddell.

La la la la la la,
La la la la la la,
Bil-ly Lid-dell.

(These lyrics were later adapted for Djimi Traore, although they were used in less glowing terms – "When the ball hits his head and ends up in row Z" being the sign-off line! The French-born Malian full-back is also the subject of another famous parody – see 'Blame It On Traore')

Billy The King
(To the tune of 'Lily The Pink' by The Scaffold)

Oh let's drink, a drink, a drink,
To Billy the king, the king, the king,
The creator of the greatest team,
For he invented professional football,
And this year we'll win the league.

Now Gerry Byrne,
Refused a tourniquet,
When he's broken his collar bone,
And they just rubbed on medicinal compound.
And Gerry goes marching on, on, ON!

Oh let's drink, a drink, a drink,
To Billy the king, the king, the king,
The creator of the greatest team,
For he invented professional football,
And this year we'll win the league.

(Another lyrical salute to Bill Shankly based on The Scaffold's reworking of the folk song 'The Ballad Of Lydia Pinkham'. The Scaffold were a comedy, poetry and music trio from Liverpool consisting of Roger McGough, John Gorman and Mike McGear – brother of a little-known Paul McCartney!)

Biscan In Our Club

(To the theme tune from the Jacob biscuits ad)

If you like Croatian players,
We've got Biscan in our club.

*(Fondly recalled by children of the '80s, the Club biscuit bar
advert turned into a latter day treat for one Anfield cult hero)*

Bjornebye In My Gang

(To the tune of 'I'm The Leader Of The Gang' by Gary Glitter)

You'll never believe it,
Come on, come on,
You'll never believe it,
Come on, come on,
You'll never believe it,
Come on, come on.

Bjornebye in my gang, my gang, my gang,
Bjornebye in my gang,
Oh yeah!

He's our left-back,
He's our left-back,
It's Stig Inge at the back, oh yeah!

*(This is a variation of the original Bjornebye Song which was
first published in legendary but now defunct fanzine Through
The Wind And Rain in the early 1990s after the Norwegian
had signed for Liverpool. To the same Gary Glitter tune it
went... 'Bjornebye's in our team, our team, our team,
Bjornebye's in our team, oh ****! He's Norwegian,
He's Norwegian...')*

Blame It On Traore

(To the tune of Michael Jackson's 'Blame It On The Boogie')

Don't blame it on the Hamann,
Don't blame it on the Biscan,
Don't blame it on the Finnan,
Blame it on Traore.

He just can't,
He just can't,
He just can't control his feet.
He just can't,
He just can't,
He just can't control his feet.

(Inspired by Djimi Traore's spectacular own-goal in the
2004/05 FA Cup defeat to Burnley)

Blaydon Races

(To the famous Geordie folk song 'Blaydon Races')

Newcastle Brown, it has to be a winner,
Twenty-five pints on a Saturday night and
twelve for Sunday dinner.
We taught the Geordies how to sing,
we taught them how to sup,
But most of all we taught them how to lift the
FA Cup.

(Originally penned by George Ridley – or Geordie Ridley as
he is better known – back in 1862, Blaydon Races famously
celebrates Geordie life, events and culture, although this
Scouse interpretation focuses more on the drinking culture
and the Reds' Cup-winning culture)

Bolo, Bolo Bolo

(To the tune of 2 Unlimited's 'No Limits')

Bolo,
Bolo Bolo,
Bolo Bolo,
Bolo, Bolo Zenden!

(The same tune was occasionally used to sing Vegard Heggem's name in the 1990s)

Build A Cabinet

(To the tune of 'American western folk ballad 'Oh My Darling Clementine')

Build a cabinet,
Build a cabinet,
Eighteen titles on the top,
Four European Cups,
Three UEFA,
Liverpool have won the lot.

(The tune was written as a response to Manchester United's 'Build A Bonfire' chant and published in The Kop Magazine, although it is clearly in need of an update now!)

Cheyrou
(To the tune of 'Chim Chim Cher-ee' from Mary Poppins fame)

Chim chiminee,

Chim chiminee,

Chim chim cheroo,

Who needs a Zidane when you've Cheyrou?

(Kopite's tongue-in-cheek chant after Gerard Houllier dubbed Bruno Cheyrou the new Zinedine Zidane on his Anfield arrival in the summer of 2002)

Come On You Mighty Reds
(To the tune of 'Those Were The Days, My Friends' recorded by Mary Hopkins and Sandie Shaw)

Come on you mighty Reds,

Come on you mighty Reds,
Come on you Reds.
Come on you mighty Reds,
Come on you mighty Reds,
Come on you mighty Reds,
Come on you Reds,
Come on you mighty Reds.

*(This simple verse is one most fans are familiar with and is
heard regularly around all sections of the ground on
matchdays)*

Corners Of Europe

From the corners of Europe,
To the shores of the Mersey,
Roma and Paris,
Wembley and Turkey.
Fightin' the fight,
For the spirit of Shankly,
One team in our city,
The team that we fight for.

[Bounce]

Liverpool, Liverpool,
Liverpool, Liverpool,
Liverpool, Liverpool,
Liverpool, Liverpool.

*(Starting out as a suggested song on an internet forum,
it soon took off in the summer of 2008 and got it's first
airing in the 4-0 pre-season friendly win over
Rangers at Ibrox in August)*

Crouch, Crouch
(To the tune of 'Lord Of The Dance')

Crouch, Crouch,
Wherever you may be,
You didn't stop at six-foot-three.
But you're not just tall,
You're a master on the ball,
And you'll win us the cup when we get to
Greece.

*(This tune was posted on Liverpool forums in the run up to
the 2007 Champions League final although it was never sung
at the match, possibly because the last line doesn't rhyme!)*

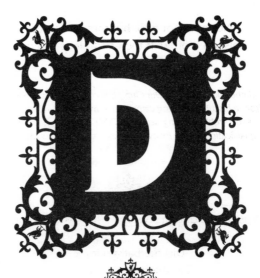

David Ngog
(To the tune of The Beatles' 'Hello, Goodbye')

You say Ngog,
I say Ngoh, Ngoh, Ngoh,
I don't know why you say Ngog,
I say Ngoh.

(Penned by Ian Collins in The Liver pub, Waterloo. There is another famous Ngog song, to the tune of Snow White's 'Heigh-ho' which mentions the contents of the young French forward's sock)

Daylight Come And I Wanna Go Home
(To the tune of 'Day-O (The Banana Boat Song)' by Harry Belafonte)

Tri-o, Tri-i-i-o,
Worthington, FA and UEFA Cups.

Not one, not two, but three trophies,
Finished it off with the Champions League.
Trio...

*(Rather like 'Biscan In Our Club', this chant takes its melody
from a biscuit marketing campaign in the '80s. It refers to the
Reds' treble-winning season of 2001, topped off by their
qualification for the following season's Champions League)*

Did The Ball Go In?

(To the tune of children's dance favourite 'The Hokey Cokey')

Did the ball go in?
Did the ball stay out?
In out, in out,
The Kop had no doubt.
We all went to Istanbul,
And Chelsea went out,
And that's what it's all about!

We're the European Champions,
The European Champions,
The European Champions,
And that's what it's all about!

[Alternative version]:

Did that ball go in?
Did that ball stay out?
In out, in out,
The Kop is in no doubt.
When Luis Garcia comes,
And scores a goal,
That's what he's all about.

Oh Jose, Jose, Jose,
Oh Jose, Jose, Jose,
Oh Jose, Jose, Jose,
He knocked your Chelsea out.

*(Heard following Luis Garcia's controversial goal that
knocked Chelsea out of the 2005 Champions League)*

Didi Hamann
(To the Batman theme tune)

Didi, didi, didi, didi,
Didi, didi, didi, didi,
Hamann!

*(A theme tune reintroduced for the German midfielder after
it was first used on Nigel Spackman)*

Diouf, Diouf, Diouf
(To the tune of 'Agadoo' by Black Lace)

El-Hadji Diouf, Diouf, Diouf,
Won't you score a goal for me,
El-Hadji Diouf, Diouf, Diouf,
Maybe two or maybe three.
With you left,
With your right,
With your head or with your knee.
El-Hadji Diouf, Diouf, Diouf,
Won't you score a goal for me.

Diouf Is On Fire

(To the tune of 'Follow Da Leader' by the Soca-Boys)

Diouf,
Diouf,
Diouf is on fire.

[Optional verse]:
If you want El-Hadj to score,
Then raise your hands higher.

*(El-Hadji Diouf's short but catchy chant was first sung on his
debut in a pre-season friendly in Le Havre in 2002 and has
now been 'borrowed' by Manchester United supporters for
their Senegalese strike prospect Mame Biram Diouf)*

Doo Wah Didi, Didi

[Chorus]:
There he was with the ball at his feet,
Singing dooh wah Didi, Hamann, Hamann.

Looked up (looked up),
Down the line (down the line),
Range of passing is sublime.

Woooh Woooh,
I knew I was falling in love,
The kind of midfielder I've been dreaming of.

There he was with the ball at his feet,
Singing dooh wah Didi, Hamann, Hamann.

Ee-aye-addio

(Based on primary school favourite 'The Farmer's In His Den')

We've won the Cup,
We've won the Cup,
Ee-aye-addio,
We've won the Cup.

*(Although seen as a generic chant for just about any team
that wins a piece of silverware, this song deserves particular
merit thanks to its Liverpool roots. Along with 'It's A Long
Way To Wembley Stadium', this was the choice chant of the
travelling Liverpool fans who witnessed first hand the club
claim its first FA Cup in 1965. TV and radio coverage of the
final helped the song gain a wider audience and it soon
became commonplace at each ground)*

Every Other Saturday

Every other Saturday's me half day off,
And it's off to the match I go,
I like to take a stroll along the Anfield Road,
Me and me old pal Joe.
I like to see the lasses with their red scarves on,
I like to hear the Kopites roar,
But I don't have to tell that best of all,
Is when we see Liverpool sc-o-o-o-ore.
We've won the English League about a
thousand times,
And UEFA was a simple do,
We've played some exhibitions in the FA Cup,
We are the Wembley Wizards too.
But when we won the European Cup in Rome,
Like we should have done years before,
We gathered down at Anfield,
Boys a hundred thousand strong,
To give the boys a welcome ho-om-me.

Kenny, ohhh Kenny,
I'd walk a million miles for one of your goals
oh Kenny,
Ohhh Kenny.

*(Another famous matchday mantra, although this one has
its origins north of the border. Written in the 1960s, the
original is the work of Rangers supporters and supposedly
signifies an era when they finished work on a Saturday
morning, many from the River Clyde shipyards, and headed
off to Ibrox for the afternoon fixture. Liverpool fans later
adapted it and it has become popular again in recent
seasons with supporters in 'Block 1892' – the singing
section at the back of the Kop)*

Fernando

(To the tune of Abba's 'Fernando')

There was someone in the box tonight,
He shines so bright, Fernando.
He was scoring goals for you and me,
For LFC, Fernando.
When he pulls on a shirt, we don't lose,
That you can bet.
Come on sing along his name again,
He's scored again, Fernando.

*(Fernando Morientes song created by Brian Gubb and aired
again during the days of Fernando Torres)*

Fields of Anfield Road

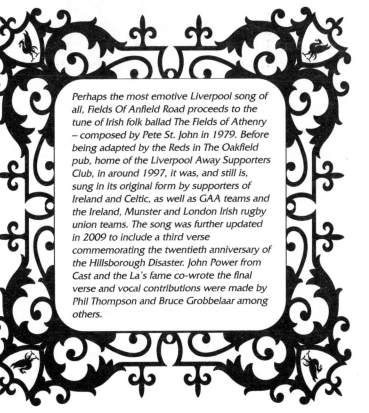

Perhaps the most emotive Liverpool song of all, Fields Of Anfield Road proceeds to the tune of Irish folk ballad The Fields of Athenry – composed by Pete St. John in 1979. Before being adapted by the Reds in The Oakfield pub, home of the Liverpool Away Supporters Club, in around 1997, it was, and still is, sung in its original form by supporters of Ireland and Celtic, as well as GAA teams and the Ireland, Munster and London Irish rugby union teams. The song was further updated in 2009 to include a third verse commemorating the twentieth anniversary of the Hillsborough Disaster. John Power from Cast and the La's fame co-wrote the final verse and vocal contributions were made by Phil Thompson and Bruce Grobbelaar among others.

Fields Of Anfield Road

Outside the Shankly Gates,
I heard a Kopite calling:
Shankly they have taken you away,
But you left a great eleven,
Before you went to heaven,
Now it's glory round the Fields of Anfield Road.

[Chorus]:
All round the Fields of Anfield Road,
Where once we watched the King Kenny play,
(And could he play).
Stevie Heighway on the wing,
We had dreams and songs to sing,
Of the glory round the Fields of Anfield Road.

Outside the Paisley Gates,
I heard a Kopite calling:
Paisley they have taken you away,
But you led the great eleven,
Back in Rome in '77,
And the Redmen they're still playing the same
way.

All round the Fields of Anfield Road,
Where once we watched the King Kenny play,
(And could he play).
Stevie Heighway on the wing,
We had dreams and songs to sing,
Of the glory round the Fields of Anfield Road.

Beside the Hillsborough flame,

I heard a Kopite mourning,
Why so many taken on that day?
Justice has never been done,
But their memory will carry on,
There'll be glory round the Fields of
Anfield Road.

All round the Fields of Anfield Road,
Where once we watched the King Kenny play,
(And could he play).
Stevie Heighway on the wing,
We had dreams and songs to sing,
Of the glory round the Fields of
Anfield Road.

(The updated Fields Of Anfield Road charity record
reached number 16 in the UK Top 40 chart on April 12,
2009 and number 14 a week later. The song was also
at number nine on the UK iTunes chart
on April 13, 2009)

Five European Cups
(To the tune of 'Ten Green Bottles')

First European Cup,
Was won in It-a-ly.
Terry Mac, Tommy Smith,
And Neal he made it three.
Moenchengladbach mangled,
By the team of Bob Paisley.
Oh the first European Cup,
We won in It-a-ly!

Second European Cup,
Was won In Wemb-er-ley.
Goodnight Bruge,
All hail King Ken-ny.
What a night in London!
Oh what a mem-or-y!
Oh the second European Cup,
We won in Wemb-er-ley!

Third European Cup,
Was won in Paris, France.
Eighty-second min-ute,
Barney Rubble took his chance.
Real Mad-rid sent packin',
In the ci-ty of romance.
Oh the third European Cup,
We won in Paris, France!

Fourth European Cup,
Was won in It-a-ly.
Brucie's wobbly legs,
And a pen by Ken-ne-dy.
Now we've four,
When before we'd only three.
Oh the fourth European Cup,
We won in It-a-ly!

Fifth European Cup,
Was won in Is-tan-bul,
Three-nil, three-all,
What a mi-ra-cle.
Now it's here forever,
To stay in Liv-er-pool.
Oh the fifth European Cup,
We won in Istanbul.

Five Times

(To the tune of 'Downtown' by Petula Clark)

At three-nil down life was feeling so down,
No one thought we'd sing – Five times.
But the fans kept on singing,
never gave up believing,
Let the night sky ring – five times.

'Cos we had Steven Gerrard in the centre of the park,
Alonso alongside him and Smicer lit the spark.
Oh how could we lose?

The players heard our rallying call,
Milan started to crumble, Jerzy saved every ball.
Now it's – five times,
Things are so great now it's – five times,
We're champions of Europe now – five times,
Everyone's singing now – five times.

Fowler's Prayer

R Fowler,
Thou art is scoring,
Robbie be thy name.
Thy transfer be done,
As a free as it is in January,
Give us this day our favourite Red,
Alonso will give you the passes,
As Carra stops those who pass against us.
Deliver us the title,
And lead us not into relegation,

For eleven is your number,
Forever and ever,
Our man.

*(Created following 'God's' return to Anfield in January 2006
and was a reworking of the Fowler's Prayer published in
Through The Wind And Rain during his first spell at the club)*

Gary Mac

Gary Mac,
Gary Mac,
Gary, Gary Mac,
Got no hair but we don't care,
Gary, Gary Mac.

Gary Macca
(To the tune of 'Alouette')

Oohhh! Gary Macca, Gary Gary Macca, Gary
Macca, Gary Gary Macca, Gary Gary Macca.
Oh we love yer baldy 'ead,
(Oh we love yer baldy 'ead),

Yer baldy 'ead
(Yer baldy 'ead),
You're Garc Mac,
(You're Gary Mac).

Oohhh! Gary Macca, Gary Gary Macca, Gary
Macca, Gary Gary Mac.

Oh we loved yer Derby goal,
(Yer Derby goal),
Oh we loved yer Barca pen,
(Yer Barca Pen),
Oh we loved yer Spurs peno,
(Yer Spurs peno),
Oh we loved yer Coventry goal,
(Yer Coventry goal),
Oh we loved yer Bradford goal,
(Yer Bradford goal),
Oh we loved yer Dortmund pen,
(Yer Dortmund pen),
Oh we love yer sweet right foot,
(Yer sweet right foot),
Oh we got you on a free
(On a free),
Oh we went and won all three
(Won all three).

Oh Gary Macca, Gary Gary Macca,
Gary Macca, Gary, Gary Mac.

*(A cult song for a cult Liverpool hero. Gary McAllister
spent just under two years at Anfield, but did enough to
merit a regular rendition of one the Kop choir's
favourite player songs)*

Gathering Cups In May

*(To the tune of children's nursery rhyme 'Here We Go
Round The Mulberry Bush')*

Here we go gathering cups in May,
Cups in May,
Cups in May,
Here we go gathering cups in May,
On a cold and frosty morning.

Glen Johnson Is Our Right-Back

*(To the tune of 'My Old Man's A Dustman'
by Lonnie Donegan)*

Glen Johnson is our right-back,
He runs on down the wing,
He whips in load of crosses,
And he puts hard tackles in.

He can cut inside defenders,
He can take it to the line,
And on his Anfield debut,
His volley was sublime.

You've seen him here for Chelsea,
He's been with Pompey too,
But now he's with the Redmen,
He's coming after you!
Oh...

*(Created by Kopite Rob Loader and declared the nation's
best football chant of 2009 by the Government-backed
'Get On' campaign)*

Going Loco With Momo Sissoko
(To the tune of 'Going Loco Down In Acapulco' by the Four Tops)

[Chorus]:
We'll be going loco with Momo Sissoko,
'Cos he's big and strong,
Yeah, we'll be going loco with Momo Sissoko,
This lad just can't do no wrong.

Feel the pressure,
Your backs against the wall,
With Momo on your heels you'll never get the ball.

'Cos we'll be going loco with Momo Sissoko,
'Cos he's big and strong,
Yeah, we'll be going loco with Momo Sissoko,
This lad just can't do no wrong.

Good King Wenceslas
(To the Christmas carol 'Good King Wenceslas')

Vegard Heggem scored a goal
on the feast of Stephen,
Vegard Heggem scored a goal
as the fans were leaving.
Liverpool they won three-one,
Carragher and Jamie.
Vegard Heggem scored a goal,
All the fans went crazy.

(Tribute to Vegard Heggem after scoring in the 3-1
Boxing Day win over Middlesbrough in 1998)

Hamann, Hamann
*(To the tune of 'I'm The Leader Of The Gang (I Am)'
by Gary Glitter)*

Hamann, Hamann,
Hamann, Hamann,
Hamann, Hamann, Hamann, DIETMAR!

Hamann, Hamann,
Hamann, Hamann,
Hamann, Hamann, Hamann, DIETMAR!

Happiness
(To the tune of 'Happiness' by Ken Dodd)

Happiness, happiness,
Now its five big-eared ones that we possess,
Oh! I thank Don Rafa that we were blessed,
On the shores of the Efes-drenched Bosphor-ess.

Happy Birthday
(Sung to the traditional tune)

Happy birthday to you,
Happy birthday to you,
Happy birthday dear Kenny,
Happy birthday to you.

*(Sung to Liverpool manager Kenny Dalglish during the 3-1
win against Man United in March 2011, two days after his
60th birthday. Kenny smiled, laughed and gave the Kop a
wave back in response)*

Harry Kewell
(To the tune of 'Daddy Cool' by Boney M)

Harry, Harry Kewell,
Harry, Harry Kewell...

*(A simple but infectious Anfield chant that accompanied the
Aussie winger to his next club, Galatasary)*

Henchoz
*(To 'Heigh-ho' from Walt Disney's animated
classic Snow White)*

Henchoz, Henchoz,
Henchoz, Henchoz, Henchoz.
When they attack,
He's always back,
Henchoz,
Henchoz, Henchoz, Henchoz.

He's...
...Carragher

He's Scouse,
He's sound,
He'll **** you with a pound,
Carragher, Carragher.

...Erik Meijer

He's big,
He's Red,
He's off his ****** head,
Erik Meijer, Erik Meijer.

...Gary Mac

He's grey,
He's old,
He's worth his weight in gold,
Gary Mac, Gary Mac.

...Igor Biscan

He's Red,
He's big,
His name begins with Ig,
Or Biscan, Or Biscan.

...Nick Barmby

He's Red,
He's white,
He scored against the *****,
Nick Barmby, Nick Barmby.

...Nigel Clough

He's Red,

He's white,

He's ******* dynamite,

Nigel Clough, Nigel Clough.

...Peter Crouch

He's big,

He's Red,

His feet stick out the bed,

Peter Crouch, Peter Crouch.

...Robbie Keane

He's quick,

He's Red,

He talks like Father Ted,

Robbie Keane, Robbie Keane.

...Sammy Lee

He's fat,

He's round,

He bounces on the ground,

Sammy Lee, Sammy Lee.

...Sander Westerveld

He's big,

He's Dutch,

We like him very much,

Westerveld, Westerveld.

...Vladimir Smicer

He's Czech,
He's great,
He's Paddy Berger's mate,
Vladimir, Vladimir.

Hey Big Didi

(To the tune of 'Hey Big Spender' by Shirley Bassey)

The minute you walked in the joint, Didi,
I could see you were Hamann of distinction,
A real big player.
Good passing, so refined,
You could always play in any midfield of mine.

So let me get right to the point, Didi,
I don't pop my cork for every player I see.
Hey big Didi, (hey big Didi),
Score another goal for me,
Da, da, da, da, da, da.

Hills Of Anfield

*(To the tune of 'Las Vegas (In The Hills Of Donegal)'
by the Irish folk rock group Goats Don't Shave)*

You may talk about Arsenal,
How they're the best a team can be,
Who's the man in the Man U top,
is Cisse better than Henry?
But ask them all where's Anfield,
It's not a mystery.

And if I could build a wall around the Merseyside,
The North and South to keep them out,
my God I'll build it tall,
Spain and Portugal, my God we'll buy them all,
We'd have the Premiership in the hills of the Kop,
Yeah, the Premiership in the hills of the Kop.

Hou Let The Reds Out?

(To the tune of Baha Men's 'Who Let The Dogs Out?')

Hou let the Reds out?
Hou, Houllier.
Hou let the Reds out?
Hou, Houllier.

*(A widely sung manager chant, partly because of the success of
the Baha Men's hit song in 2000 – it was the UK's fourth
biggest selling single that year – but mainly because
the treble campaign led by Gerard Houllier in
2001 had the Kop in good voice)*

Houllier, Houllier

(To the tune of Boney M's 'Holiday')

Houllier, Houllier,
Gerard Houllier.
He's a man from France,
Who makes us dance,
Gerard Houllier.

*(One of several songs afforded to our former French manager.
The reference to "There's A Man From France" comes from one
of the other songs of the same title)*

Ian Rush

Ian Rush,
Ian Rush,
Ian, Ian Rush.
He gets the ball,
He scores a goal,
Ian, Ian Rush.

Igor Biscan

Igor Biscan,
Is a giant of a man,
Plays in the middle with Hamann.
Try and catch him if you can,
Igor Biscan, he's our man.

(Often accompanied to the sound of "EEEEEEEEEGOR!")

Igor Biscan's Our Hero
(To the nursery rhyme 'This Old Man')

Two-nil down,
Four-two up,
Igor Biscan wrapped it up,
And he didn't know what to do,
When he scored that goal,
Igor Biscan's our hero.

(Sung after his wonder goal at Fulham in October 2004)

I'm Sticking With You
*(To the tune of 'I'm Sticking With You'
by The Velvet Underground)*

I'm sticking with you,
'Cos you're Bruno Cheyrou.
Whatever you wanna do,
We're gonna love you.

In Dublin's Fair City
(To the tune of popular Irish song 'Molly Malone')

In Dublin's fair city,
Where the girls are so pretty,
I first set my eyes on sweet Molly Malone.
As she wheeled her wheel-barrow,
Through the streets broad and narrow,
Crying…

[clap, clap]
[clap, clap, clap]
[clap, clap, clap, clap]

ST. JOHN!

(This song retains all the original lyrics from the opening verse of this unofficial anthem of Dublin City, the one key change being the insertion of the clapping and, of course, the loud proclamation of Anfield legend Ian St John. The 'St John' chant is only bestowed on Liverpool's greatest goalscorers by the Kop with 'Dalglish', 'Fowler', 'Owen' and 'Torres' the only others to have their names sung after the famous staccato handclap)

Istanbul 05
(To the tune of 'Horse With No Name' by America)

On the fifth part of the journey...
well we had to get past Milan,
But Maldini scored and Crespo roared
and the **** had hit the fan.
Any other side and they'd call it quits,
but that's not the Liverpool Way,
On stepped Didi and up stepped Stevie
and the Reds began to play.

[Chorus]:
See we went to Istanbul for a football game,
Where destiny called us again.
Three-nil down...The whole world had called it a day,
But they hadn't counted on...The Liverpool way.

La la la la la la la, la la la, la la,
La la la la la la la, la la la, la la.

After two goals in the Ataturk,
me face began to turn Red,
Third goal, and the Milanese,
thought they'd put us to bed,
But a story got told of how we just wouldn't fold,
While refusing to believe we were dead.

See we went to Istanbul for a football game,
Where destiny called us again.
Three-nil down...The whole world had called it a day,
But they hadn't counted on...The Liverpool way.

La la la la la la la la, la la la, la la,
La la la la la la la, la la la, la la.

After 90 minutes then extra time, it finally ended 3-3,
There'd been praying souls and comeback goals from
Stevie, Vladi and Xabi.
Pulling Jerzy near, Carra said in his ear:
"do the jelly legs and give a cough",
Then Shevchenko missed and we all got ******,
'cos the party kicked right off.

See we went to Istanbul for a football game,
Where destiny called us again.
Three-nil down...The whole world had called it a day,
But they hadn't counted on...The Liverpool way.

La la la la la la la la, la la la, la la,
La la la la la la la, la la la, la la.

La la la la la la la la, la la la, la la,
La la la la la la la, la la la, la la.

Istanbul 05

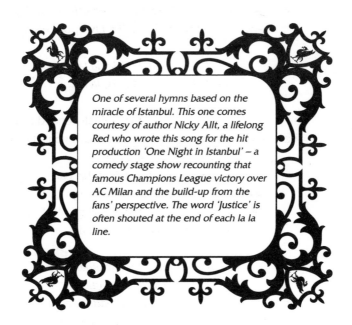

One of several hymns based on the miracle of Istanbul. This one comes courtesy of author Nicky Allt, a lifelong Red who wrote this song for the hit production 'One Night in Istanbul' – a comedy stage show recounting that famous Champions League victory over AC Milan and the build-up from the fans' perspective. The word 'Justice' is often shouted at the end of each la la line.

Istanbul, Istanbul

Istanbul,
Istanbul,
We're the greatest team in Europe and
we're going to Istanbul.

Istanbul Is Wonderful

(To the tune of 'When The Saints Go Marching In')

Oh Istanbul,
(Oh Istanbul),
It's wonderful,
(It's wonderful)
Oh Istanbul is wonderful,
It's full of mosques, kebabs and Scousers,
Oh Istanbul is wonderful.

It's A Long Way To Wembley Stadium

(To the tune 'It's A Long Way To Tipperary')

It's a long way to Wembley stadium,
It's a long way to go,
It's a long way to Wembley stadium,
To see the greatest team I know.
So it's goodbye Upper Parly,
Farewell Clayton Square,
It's a long, long way to Wembley stadium,
But Liverpool will be there.

It's Only On Loan

(To the tune of 'Sloop John B' by the Beach Boys)

It's only on loan,
It's only on loan,
In ancient Greece,
We'll bring it back home.

(Created ahead of the 2007 Champions League final in Athens)

Jari Litmanen
(To the tune of 'Seasons In The Sun' by Terry Jacks)

We have joy,
We have fun,
We have Jari Litmanen.
He's got style,
He's got flair,
Got a mullet,
We don't care.

Jari's All You Need
(To the tune of 'All You Need Is Love' by The Beatles)

Jari Litmanen – da da da da da,
Jari Litmanen – da da da da da,
Jari Litmanen – nen,
Jari's all you need.

Javier Mascherano

(To the tune of The White Stripes' 'Seven Nation Army')

Oh, oh, oh oh-o-oh,
Oh, oh, oh oh-o-oh
Jav-ier Mas-cher-ano, Jav-ier Masc-her-ano.

Jerzy Dudek In Our Goal

(To the tune of 'Camptown Races')

Jerzy Dudek in our goal, Dudek, Dudek.
Jerzy Dudek in our goal, Poland's number one.
Sander's been and gone, Dudek's number one.
Jerzy Dudek in our goal, Poland's number one.

*(Tribute to Liverpool's 2005 Champions League final saviour.
The same tune is also sung to the lyrics: "6ft Pole in our goal,
Du-dek, Du-dek, 6ft Pole in our goal, do dah do dah dey")*

Jimmy Plaice

Jimmy Plaice,
Jimmy Plaice,
Jimmy Plaice.

*(Chanted during Liverpool's 1980 League Cup trip to the
fishing town of Grimsby. It was the climax to a series of
spontaneous player puns involving fish. This one refers to
Jimmy Case while others included Kenny Dog-fish,
Swordfish Souness, Sting-Ray Kennedy and "There's only
one Phil Eel", while "You only win when you're fishing'
kicked off the chanting along with
"We are the famous carpites")*

John Arne Riise (I)
(To the tune of 'Hey! Baby' by DJ Otzi)

Johhhhnnnnnn Arne Riise,
Ooooh ahhhh,
I wanna knoo-ooo-oow,
How you scored that goal.

(Testament to the incredible shooting ability of our former left-sided Norwegian. Although some believe it to have come about from his super strike against Manchester United in November 2001, his goal against Everton at Goodison two months earlier was the inspiration and it was first sung en-masse when he scored against Newcastle at St James' Park in September 2001)

John Arne Riise (II)
(To the tune of 'Waltzing Matilda')

John Arne Riise, John Arne Riise,
Ran down the wing and he scored at the Pit,
And we sang, and we danced,
And we shook the ground that's made of wood,
John Arne Riise scored against the ****!

John Houlding
(To the tune 'The Irish Rover', recorded by The Pogues)

In the year of our Lord, eighteen ninety and two,
John Houlding evicted the Blues,
From their Anfield abode on the Walton Breck Road,
He was tired of seeing them lose.
Years behind in rent all their money was spent,

A bank that held nothing but zeros,
But Houlding instead built a team dressed in red,
Liverpool his Anfield heroes.

*(Fans pay homage to Liverpool's founder, although technically
when he created the team, they were dressed in blue and white)*

Johnny Barnes

(To the tune of 'Buffalo Soldier' by Bob Marley)

Oh his father was a soldier,
(Oh his father was a soldier),
He couldn't play the football,
(He couldn't play the football),
His son he played for Watford,
(His son he played for Watford),
But now he play for Liverpool,
(But now he play for Liverpool).
His name is Johnny Barnes,
(His name is Johnny Barnes),
He comes from Jamaica,
(He comes from Jamaica),
And if you read the papers,
(And if you read the papers),
He's going to Italia,
(He's going to Italia),
Oh no no, no no no, no no no, no no no no.

Johnny Barnes Went That Way

Johnny Barnes went that way,
Four defenders went that way.

Johnny On The Ball

[Chorus]:
We love John Barnes,
We love John Barnes,
We love John Barnes,
We love Johnny on the ball.

He's fantastic,
Legs elastic,
He stands proud while all defenders fall.
Shout it loud like,
Shout it all around like,
Shout it in the ground like,
Or anywhere at all, that:

We love John Barnes,
We love John Barnes,
We love John Barnes,
We love Johnny on the ball.

Josemi

Josemi, woooaahh,
Josemi, woooaahh,
He came from Malaga,
To play with Carragher.

Josemi, woooaahh,
Josemi, woooaahh,
He came from Malaga,
To play with Carragher.

Just Can't Get Enough

(To the tune of 'Just Can't Get Enough' by Depeche Mode)

His name is Luis Suarez,
He wears the famous Red,
I just can't get enough,
I just can't get enough.

When he scores a volley,
And when he scores a head,
I just can't get enough,
I just can't get enough.

He scores a goal and the Kop go wild,
And I just can't seem to get enough SUAREZ.

der der der der der der der, der der der der der der
der, der der der der der der
LUIS SUAREZ

*('Just Can't Get Enough' was a hit with Celtic fans in 2010/11
and Kopites came up with a Suarez song to the same tune.
There are a few lyrical variations, but this became the most
popular version after it was sung and videoed on a coach
on the way back from a 1-0 win at Chelsea and
viewed by over 70,000 people on YouTube)*

Keane For A Fiesta
(To the tune of 'Fiesta' by the Pogues)

Oh Robbie Keane grew up in Dublin,
With Fowler's poster above his bed,
He's played for Inter, Leeds & Tottenham too,
But he has always been a Red.

He wears the sacred number seven,
And with his pace teams will be scared,
He'll do a cartwheel and run towards the Kop,
As he kisses the Liverbird.

Kenny D, The Pride Of Liverpool

(Liverpool...Dalglish...)
(Liverpool...Dalglish...)

It's the time you've got to win, 'cos you know
you've got it right.
'77 we lost Kevin, but Kenny joined the side.
Kenny's goal made sure we hold the
European Cup,
Look what he's done, we're number one,
Easy! Easy!

[Chorus]:
Wo-ow here we go,
Nothing's gonna stop us now.
We've got the world at our feet,
And with Dalglish in the seat,
We'll do it all again somehow.
(Liverpool!)
Wo-ow here we go,
We Never Walk Alone, it's true.
With Kenny we ought to be,
We're very proud to be,
The pride of Liverpool.

He was capped more times by the Scottish side
than anyone else has been,
When he played in red, Paisley said he's the
best he'd ever seen.
The league, European, and the FA Cup,
He's done it all.
With Kenny D it's got to be,
Easy! Easy!

Wo-ow here we go,
Nothing's gonna stop us now.
We've got the world at our feet,

And with Dalglish in the seat,
We'll do it all again somehow.
(Liverpool!)
Wo-ow here we go,
We Never Walk Alone, it's true.
With Kenny we ought to be,
We're very proud to be,
The pride of Liverpool.

Four years on we're going strong, twice manager of the year,
In the cup they sing "Kenny's King", at Anfield they're sincere.
Guaranteed through tragedy You'll Never Walk Alone
And you can see with Kenny D,
It's Easy! Easy!

Wo-ow here we go,
Nothing's gonna stop us now.
We've got the world at our feet,
And with Dalglish in the seat,
We'll do it all again somehow.
(Liverpool!)
Wo-ow here we go,
We Never Walk Alone, it's true.
With Kenny we ought to be,
We're very proud to be,
The pride of Liverpool.

(Liverpool, Liverpool, Liverpool, Liverpool)

[Repeat chorus]

(Liverpool's 1989 side team up with Peter Howitt for one of club's least
recognised recorded singles. The background chanting is provided by
The Kop during the Reds' 5-2 League Cup victory over Wigan on
September 19, 1989)

Kuyt Fever
(To the tune of 'Night Fever' by the Bee Gees)

Kuyt Fever,
Kuyt Fever,
He knows how to do it.

(The mispronunciation over Dirk Kuyt's surname inspired this attempt around the bars of Anfield)

Kuyt, Kuyt, Let It All Out
(To the tune 'Shout' by Tears For Fears)

Kuyt, Kuyt, let it all out,
He's big and he's Dutch and he puts it about.

La Rafa
(To the tune of 'La Bamba')

Ra Ra Ra Ra-fa Benitez,
Ra Ra Ra Ra-fa Benitez,
Xabi Alonso, Garcia and Nunez (and Josemi, and Josemi!)
Ra-fa Benitez, Ra-fa Benitez..

(The third line was changed from 'Nunez' to 'Reina' in 2005/06 and then from 'Garcia' to 'Torres' in 2006/07. A Spanish lyrically-adequate replacement for Xabi Alonso, who left in 2009, was never discovered under Rafa)

L-I-V
(To the tune of 'Jesus Christ Superstar')

L-I-V,
E-R-P,
Double-O L,
Liverpool FC.

Liverbird Upon My Chest

This instantly recognisable anthem has grown in stature as each momentous success is scripted to form another verse. Originally called 'The Ballad of the Green Berets' and featuring in a John Wayne film, the patriotic tune was written as a Liverpool song in the mid-'80s by Phil Aspinall and only went as far as the verse recounting the club's 1986 FA Cup success over Everton. It's believed to have first been sung during a visit to the capital during the 1986/87 season, possibly White Hart Lane.

Liverbird Upon My Chest
(To the tune of 'Ballad of the Green Berets')

Here's a song about a football team,
The greatest team you've ever seen,
A team that play Total Football,
They've won the league, Europe and all.

[Chorus]:
A Liverbird upon my chest,
We are the men of Shankly's best,
A team that plays the Liverpool way,
And wins the championship in May.

With Kenny Dalglish on the ball,
He was the greatest of them all,
And Ian Rush, four goals or two,
Left Evertonians feeling blue.

A Liverbird upon my chest,
We are the men of Shankly's best,
A team that plays the Liverpool way,
And wins the championship in May.

Now if you go down Goodison Way,
Hard luck stories you hear each day,
There's not a trophy to be seen,
'Cos Liverpool have swept them clean.

A Liverbird upon my chest,
We are the men of Shankly's best,
A team that plays the Liverpool way,
And wins the championship in May.

Now on the glorious 10th of May,
There's laughing Reds on Wembley Way,
We're full of smiles and joy and glee,
It's Everton one and Liverpool three.

A Liverbird upon my chest,
We are the men of Shankly's best,
A team that plays the Liverpool way,
And wins the championship in May.

Now on the 20th of May,
We're laughing still on Wembley Way,
Those Evertonians are feeling blue,
It's Liverpool three and Everton two.

A Liverbird upon my chest,
We are the men of Shankly's best,
A team that plays the Liverpool way,
And wins the championship in May.

And as we sang round Goodison Park,
With crying Blues all in a nark,
They're probably crying still,
At Liverpool five and Everton nil.

A Liverbird upon my chest,
We are the men of Shankly's best,
A team that plays the Liverpool way,
And wins the championship in May.

We Remember them with pride,
Those mighty Reds of Shankly's side,
And Kenny's boys of '88,
There's never been a side so great.

A Liverbird upon my chest,
We are the men of Shankly's best,
A team that plays the Liverpool way,
And wins the championship in May.

Now back in 1965,
When great Bill Shankly was alive,
We're playing Leeds, the score's one-one,
When it fell to the head of Ian St John.

A Liverbird upon my chest,
We are the men of Shankly's best,
A team that plays the Liverpool way,
And wins the championship in May.

On April 15th '89,
What should have been a joyous time,
Ninety-six friends, we all shall miss,
And all the Kopites want justice,
(JUSTICE!)

A Liverbird upon my chest,
We are the men of Shankly's best,
A team that plays the Liverpool way,
And wins the championship in May.

Liv-er-pool

And it's Liv-er-pool,
Liverpool FC,
We're by FAR the greatest team,
The world has ever seen.

Liverpool *[Clap, Clap, Clap]*

Li-ver-pool,
[clap, clap, clap]
Li-ver-pool,
[clap, clap, clap]

[Repeat several times]

(Chants don't come simpler than this, nor do they hold as much significance, for this is reckoned to be the song that gave birth to the singing Kop. Although countless teams adopt the format, its roots in this country come from Liverpool supporters who, in turn, owe a debt of thanks to a bunch of Brazilians. As the World Cup transmitted to the homes of many for the first time in 1962, Brazilian fans were heard chanting "Bra-zil, cha, cha, cha" during the tournament. It clearly inspired the Anfield faithful for upon resumption of the First Division, Liverpool's first game of the season against Blackpool drew a crowd of over 51,000, with over half congregating on the Kop. Everyone was there with their rattles and scarves all intent on making a noise when suddenly someone started to shout Liv-er-pool followed by what they called staccato clapping. The rest is history with the simple ditty now the staple song for most clubs)

Liverpool Are Magic

Liverpool are magic,
Everton are tragic,
La la la la.

(A simple chant already in existence before the late great Emlyn Hughes was credited with coining the phrase. He did, however, bring it to prominence when, during the club's 1977 European Cup homecoming, he greeted the crowd by picking up the mic and uttering those very words, encouraging the fans to break out in chorus)

Liverpool Will Marmalise Milan
(To the tune of Irish folk ballad 'Kelly Of Killane')

What's the news, what's the news,
Oh my brave Anfield fans,
As you wait for the game to begin,
Milne and Byrne are both hurt,
But each noble red shirt,
Will pray tonight that Liverpool will win.
Oh my boys they're the pride of the whole
Merseyside,
They're the greatest of heroes to a man,
So fling your favours aloft,
And give three rousing cheers that,
Liverpool will marmalise Milan.

Tell me who is the giant,
With the black curly hair,
He who stands at the head of your band?
Seven feet is his height,
With some inches to spare.
And he looks like a king in command,
Ron Yeats is his name,
The best skipper in the game,
He's the greatest of heroes, what a man!
So fling your favours aloft,
And give three rousing cheers that,
Liverpool will marmalise Milan.

Now in three minutes flat,
At the drop of a hat,
Geoff Strong passed the ball to Callaghan,
Well our wishes all came true,
When young Roger Hunt went through,

And should have heard the roar from the fans.
Well boys they're the pride of the whole
Merseyside,
They're the greatest of heroes to a man,
So fling your favours aloft,
And give three rousing cheers that,
Liverpool will marmalise Milan.

*(Performed ahead of the 1964/65 European Cup semi-final,
second leg, which Liverpool lost 4-3 on aggregate)*

Liverpool (We're Never Gonna Stop)

[Chorus]:
Oh oh oh, oh oh oh,
Liverpool, we're never gonna stop.
Oh oh oh, oh oh oh,
Liverpool, we're never gonna stop.

With you all behind us, we just can't go wrong,
We've got the rhythm, if you've got the song.
So raise your voices, and we'll raise our game,
Liverpool, Liverpool, long may we reign.

Oh oh oh, oh oh oh,
Liverpool, we're never gonna stop.
Oh oh oh, oh oh oh,
Liverpool, we're never gonna stop.

When we play together, we just can't be beat,
Shout 'no surrender', don't mention defeat.
The long road to glory is trodden by few,
There's no turning back, we're winning for you.

Oh oh oh, oh oh oh,
Liverpool, we're never gonna stop.
Oh oh oh, oh oh oh,
Liverpool, we're never gonna stop.

L is the League, is it number 14?
I – we're invincible, know what I mean?
V is for victory, E – ever more,
R – we're the Reds, and we're ready to score.
P is for Paisley, what more can we say?
Double – O, L – Liverpool,
Liverpool, we're on the way.

Oh oh oh, oh oh oh,
Liverpool, we're never gonna stop.
Oh oh oh, oh oh oh,
Liverpool, we're never gonna stop.

Oh oh oh, oh oh oh,
Liverpool, we're never gonna stop.
Oh oh oh, oh oh oh,
Liverpool, we're never gonna stop.

(Official club anthem, released as a double A side in 1983.
It reached number 54 in the UK charts. The song was
written, performed and produced by former Hollies
guitarist/singer Terry Sylvester, an Allerton-raised Red who
almost signed for Liverpool as a schoolboy when invited
for a trial at Melwood by then trainer Bob Paisley. Now
living and performing in America, he was recently
inducted into the Rock & Roll Hall Of Fame and attended
the ceremony in his Liverpool shirt. Terry was in the
Leppings Lane during the Hillsborough disaster and is a
cousin of former Everton boss Joe Royle. He remains in
touch with many former players, including
Steve Nicol and Phil Neal)

London Bridge Is Falling Down

London Bridge is falling down,
Falling down, falling down,
London Bridge is falling down,
Poor old Chelsea.

Build it up with Red and White,
Red and White,
Red and White.
Build it up with Red and White,
Poor old Chelsea.

*(Originated during the 1965/66 season when Liverpool beat
Chelsea 2-1 at Anfield to seal a seventh title. Some make
the reference more obvious by substituting London Bridge
for Stamford Bridge)*

Look Out Wembley Here We Come

Look out Wembley here we come,
With our best shooting boots on.
The Cup ties have started,
You think it's a joke,
Each morning at training,
This is what the players are saying,
When at your toe, the ball you get,
Crack it right into the net,
And we'll get to Wembley yet,
Look out Wembley here we come.

See those twinkling toes of Payne,
Up to his old tricks again,
A flick and a twist,
He's away up the wing.
The half-back left standing,
See he's also beat the full-back,
Then across the centre will go,
Directly to Liddell's toe,
Crack! And the rest you know,
Look out Wembley here we come!

Lucas Leiva!

Lucas Leiva, Lucas Leiva, ay, ay!
Lucas Leiva, Lucas Leiva, ay, ay!

Luis Garcia
(To the tune of 'You Are My Sunshine')

Luis Garcia,
He drinks sangria,
He came from Barca,
To bring us joy.
He's five-foot seven,
He's football heaven,
So please don't take our Luis away.

*(Dedicated to Liverpool's former diminutive Spanish winger.
His huge rapport with fans, thanks to the goals that got the
Reds to Istanbul in 2005, has ensured it lives long in the
memory and is still sung to this day)*

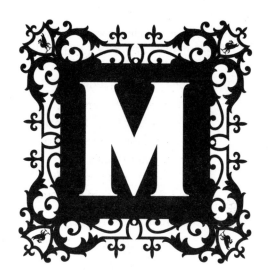

Made For Shooting
(To the tune of 'These Boots Are Made For Walkin'
by Nancy Sinatra)

We'll all sing and raise our glasses up,
When we win the European Cup.
We've got the greatest side in the land,
And we're all known as Shankly's happy band.

[Chorus]:
These boots are made for shooting,
And that's just what they'll do,
And when we get to Hungary,
They'll score a goal or two.

They keep saying we'll do something new,
And rest assured that's what we're gonna do.

When Ian St John and Roger come inside,
They'll give the Honved goalie such a fright.

These boots are made for shooting,
And that's just what they'll do,
And when we get to Hungary,
They'll score a goal or two.

Something else that really makes us sing,
Is Callaghan and Thompson on the wing.
Their centre-forward may find things are cloudy,
When he finds himself beneath big Rowdy.

These boots are made for shooting,
And that's just what they'll do,
And when we get to Hungary,
They'll score a goal or two.

(Sung ahead of the 1965/66 Cup Winners' Cup second
round match against Honved. The game ended goalless but
the Reds progressed courtesy of a 2-0 win at Anfield)

Mark Gonzalez
(To the tune of 'Delilah' by Tom Jones)

Mark, Mark, Mark Gonzalez,
Mark, Mark, Mark Gonzalez.
So before immigration break down the door,
You can't take Gonzalez, he isn't illegal no
more.

(Sung after South African-born, Chilean winger Mark
Gonzalez was finally granted a work permit to play for the
Reds – one year after agreeing a move to Anfield!)

Markus Babbel

(To the tune of 'Rivers of Babylon' by Boney M)

We've got Markus Babbel on,
Plays at the back,
He's a great defender,
Likes to attack.

*(Our former German right-back was honoured with his own
song during a hugely impressive 2000/01 season. Although
later struck down by the debilitating Guillain-Barré
syndrome, Babbel admits one of his favourite Anfield
memories was hearing the song upon his return. "There was
the Charity Shield game against Arsenal after my illness. I
came on for the last ten minutes and the whole stadium
stood up to sing my name and applaud me. It was a
fantastic reception and it meant so much to me.")*

Matchstalk Men

*(To the theme tune of Brian and Michael's 'Matchstalk Men
and Matchstalk Cats and Dogs' about Salford artist Lowry)*

Now sit right down and I'll talk to you,
A song I'd like to sing to you,
It's all about a team called Liverpool,
Oh we had an end called the Anfield Road,
And no surrender was our code,
And it's been that way,
For over a hundred years.

We went to London town with Liverpool red and white,
We went to Rome and we drank and we danced and we sang all night.
Now we take our banners and wait outside the Bill Shankly gates,
To greet the greatest team, a team called Liverpool.

Maxi

(To the theme tune from 'Heartbeat' originally by Buddy Holly)

Dah-da da da da,
Dah-da da da da,
Dah-da da da da,
Dah-da da da da,
Maxi,
Maxi Rodriguez runs down the wing for me.
Dah-da da da da,
Dah-da da da da…

(First sung during the 3-0 victory over West Ham in April 2010)

McManaman!

(To The Muppets theme tune)

Do do de do de do do (McManaman!)
Do do de do de do (McManaman!)
Do do de do de do do do-de do de do de do do
(McManaman!)

Men Of Anfield

(To the tune of Welsh military march song 'Men of Harlech')

Stevie Heighway's always running,
John Toshack is always scoring,
Then you'll hear the Kopites roaring,
Toshack is our king.

Men of Anfield here's our story,
We have gone from great to glory,
We're the greatest team in Europe,
Toshack is our king.

[Alternative version]:

Paddy Berger's always running,
Michael Owen's always scoring,
Then you hear the Kopites roaring,
Fowler is our king.

Men of Anfield here's our story,
We have gone from great to glory,
We're the greatest team in Europe,
Fowler is our king.

Michael Owen
(To the tune of 'Michael Row The Boat Ashore')

Michael Owen scores our goals, hallelujah,
Michael Owen scores our goals, hallelujah.

Michael Owen Score A Goal For Me
(To the tune of Rene & Renata's 'Save Your Love')

Michael Owen score a goal for me,
Just like the two you scored in Italy.
Score another like in Roma,
Then this lot can **** off home-a.
Michael Owen score a goal for me.

Mickey Marsh

(To the 'Mickey Mouse Song')

M-I-C,
K-E-Y,
M-A-R-S-H,
Mickey Marsh, Mickey Marsh.

Mo Sissoko

(To the tune 'Buffalo Soldier' by Bob Marley)

His daddy was a soldier,
(His daddy was a soldier),
He couldn't kick a football,
(He couldn't kick a football),
His son he played for Malia,
(His son he played for Malia),
Now he plays for Liverpool,
(Now he plays for Liverpool),
His name is Mo Sissoko,
(His name is Mo Sissoko),
He wouldn't wear his goggles,
(He wouldn't wear his goggles),
He nearly signed for Everton,
(He nearly signed for Everton),
He must have lost his marbles,
(He must have lost his marbles),

Mo Mo Mo, Mo Sissoko, Mo Mo Mo, Mo Sissoko,
Mo Mo Mo, Mo Sissoko, Mo Mo Mo, Mo Sissoko.

*(A re-make of the Johnny Barnes song that gets aired
as a prelude to 'The Mo Mo Mo Song')*

Mor, Mor, Mor

(To the tune 'More, More, More' by Andrea True Connection/Rachel Stevens)

Mor, Mor, Mor,
Morientes,
Morientes.
Mor, Mor, Mor,
Morientes,
Morientes.

My Father's Scarf

(To the tune of Irish Republican folk song 'The Broad Black Brimmer')

There's a scarf that's been hanging in what's known as father's room,
A scarf that is so simple in its style.
And it's not made of gold nor silk and it's faded from its bloom,
But my mother has preserved it all the while.
One day she let me try it on,
A wish of mine for years.
And as she placed the scarf around me neck, she nearly cried,
As she gazed upon the stripes of white and red.

[Chorus]:
It's being to Reykjavik and Dusseldorf,
Paris, Wembley and to Rome.
He wore it every week when he went to watch the Reds,
It's been to Glasgow, Barcelona and Cologne.
Thick red stripes with tassels frayed and torn,
And badges from the bottom to the top.
And right there I made a vow that every
Saturday from now,
I'd wear my father's scarf upon the Kop.

It's the scarf my father wore one evening long ago,
When the fog came down and smothered Amsterdam.
It's the scarf he waved above his head, at Hampden Park,
The scarf he nearly lost when in Milan.
He wore it on the day that Rowdy Yeats picked up the Cup,
As the Kop sang out "You'll Never Walk Alone."
And in Wembley as we danced,
Rome and Paris, that's in France.
When we brought the European Cup back home.

It's being to Reykjavik and Dusseldorf,
Paris, Wembley and to Rome.
He wore it every week when he went to watch the Reds,
It's being to Glasgow, Barcelona and Cologne.
Thick red stripes with tassels frayed and torn,
And badges from the bottom to the top.
And right there I made a vow that every
Saturday from now,
I'd wear my father's scarf upon the Kop.

My Liverpool

[Chorus]:
My Liverpool, the Kop will always rule,
We'll show the world how football's played.
My Liverpool, the Kop will always rule,
Come and join us!
We're gonna take the cup away!

Hear the ground resounding when we walk out on the field,
Ding dong, the Reds are back in town.

All around the hope's abounding and we know the
future's sealed,
For Liverpool the sun is shining down.

My Liverpool, the Kop will always rule,
We'll show the world how football's played.
My Liverpool, the Kop will always rule,
Come and join us!
We're gonna take the cup away!

Flags are waving brightly and we've got them on the run,
We know a goal is coming soon.
They could try to mark us tightly but we know the game is won,
The lads of Anfield Road don't need much room.

My Liverpool, the Kop will always rule,
We'll show the world how football's played.
My Liverpool, the Kop will always rule,
Come and join us!
We're gonna take the cup away!

Neil Mellor

(To the tune 'Yellow' by Coldplay)

We found a star,
He'll score a goal for you,
He doesn't like Man U,
And he's called Mellor.

The clock it said,
That it was 92,
Oh what a thing to do,
And it was all Mellor.

*(Created in honour of Neil Mellor's 25-yard super strike
deep in injury-time to give the Reds a 2-1 Premier League
win over Arsenal at Anfield in November 2004)*

O Come All Ye Faithful

O come all ye faithful,
Joyful and triumphant,
O come ye,
O come ye,
To Anfield.

Come and behold them,
They're the Kings of Europe.
O come let us adore them,
O come let us adore them,
O come let us adore them,
Li-i-verpool.

Oh Campione

A cult chant developed for the 2007 Champions League campaign. After seeing a film of PAOK fans singing it at their club's AGM, Liverpool fans hoping to go to Greece for the final were impressed enough to coin their own words and emulate the power generated by the Greek fans. It soon took off and provided the catalyst for similar chants, including Sotirios Kyrgiakos' warmly received player song.

Oh Campione

Ooooh Campione,
The one and only,
We're Liverpool,
They say our days are numbered,
We're not famous anymore,
But Scousers rule the country,
Like we've always done before.
Ooooh Campione.

Oh Kyrgiakos

(To the tune of 'Oh Campione')

Oooh Kyrgiakos, the one and only,
He is a loon!
We thought his days were numbered,
Now he plays here every week,
We can't pronounce his surname,
So we call him Nick The Greek.
Oooh Kyrgiakos.

*(The arrival of Sotirios Kyrgiakos in the summer of 2009
caused a bit of head scratcher with Liverpool's lead lyricists,
but a few months on, and a few commanding performances
from the club's first ever Greek player, inspired this
reworking of Oh Campione)*

Oh Liverpool Bill

(To the tune of 'Liverpool Lou' by The Scaffold)

[Chorus]:
Oh Liverpool Bill, you're our Liverpool Bill.
Your name is a legend of courage and skill,
You gave us the league, all the cups and the thrills,
And that's why we love you our Liverpool Bill.

Anfield will always remember with pride,
The Scot who commanded the Liverpool side.
As sharp as a razor – his wit and his voice,
His love of the game made him Liverpool's choice.

Oh Liverpool Bill, you're our Liverpool Bill.
Your name is a legend of courage and skill,
You gave us the league, all the cups and the thrills,
And that's why we love you our Liverpool Bill.

Bill you will never be walking alone,
The Kop will be with you away or at home.
As long as we breathe we'll remember you still,
Oh thank you forever our Liverpool Bill.

Oh Liverpool Bill, you're our Liverpool Bill.
Your name is a legend of courage and skill,
You gave us the league, all the cups and the thrills,
And that's why we love you our Liverpool Bill.

*(Kopites profess their love for the legendary Bill Shankly with a
unique take on The Scaffold's 1974 No.7 UK hit single
'Liverpool Lou' which was recorded with
Paul McCartney and The Wings)*

Oh Ronny Ronny

Ronny, oh Ronny Ronny,
Oh Ronny Ronny, Oh Ronny Rosenthal, Oi!

*(The simple but stirring chant for the Israeli who became an
instant cult hero at Anfield. The song was so popular, the
format was assigned to a fellow countryman in the song
'Oh Yossi Yossi' before his move to Chelsea)*

Oh When The Reds Go Marching In

(To the tune 'When The Saints Go Marching In')

Oh when the Reds,
(Oh when the Reds),
Go marching in,
(Go marching in),
Oh when the Reds go marching in,
I wanna be in that number,
Oh when the Reds go marching in.

*(Another must mantra for matchdays. Based on an old
gospel tune revived by the traditional jazz bands of the
early '60s, it was an instant terrace classic, and has since
been copied by other clubs, including Southampton where
many believe it originated. Some believe the song started
life as tribute to the great Ian St John)*

Oh Sami Sami

Oh, Sami, Sami,
Sami, Sami, Sami, Sami Hyypia.

Oh Yossi Yossi

Yossi, oh Yossi Yossi,
Oh Yossi Yossi, oh Yossi Benayoun Oi!

One Andy Carroll

One Andy Carroll,
There's only one Andy Carroll,
One Andy Carroll...

(Sung in the 3-0 win against Man City in April 2011 when Any Carroll scored his first two goals for the Reds. Although the chant lacks inventiveness, it was used for others in the past, notably Michael Owen, in the early stages of their Liverpool careers while a better chant is developed)

One-Nil Down, Two-One Up

(To the nursery rhyme 'This Old Man')

One-nil down, two-one up,
Michael Owen won the Cup,
When a top class Paddy pass,
Gave the lad the ball,
Poor old Arsenal won **** all.

(Michael Owen is immortalised in Kop chorus after his late double at the Millennium Stadium in 2001 ripped the FA Cup from the Gunners' grasp. The song's popularity helped craft 'Igor Biscan's Our Hero')

Our Mighty Emlyn

(To the tune of 'Mighty Quinn' by Manfred Mann)

Come all without,
Come all within,
You ain't seen nothing,
Like the Mighty Emlyn.

[Alternative version]:

Come all within,
Come all without,
You ain't seen nothing,
Like our Mighty Dirk Kuyt.

*(The rousing rendition honouring our former captain and
two-time European Cup winner regularly reverberated
around Anfield during the '70s, while nowadays, Dirk Kuyt
is afforded Crazy Horse's simple four-line stanza)*

Over The Hills And Far Away

*(To the tune 'Over The Hills And Far Away'
as used in the Sharpe series)*

The Kings of the Kop come and go,
We stand as judge by what we know,
Our history trophy display,
Those wonderful nights in bonny may.
O'er hills we still reign,
Across Italy, Portugal and Spain,
King Rafa commands and we obey,
O'er the hills and far away.

Pass And Move
(It's The Liverpool Groove)

Straight out the boot room,
To Wembley, our second home,
We come to conquer, no we never walk alone.
Read out my name, the cream of the crop,
Drawing all our strength from the roar of the Kop.
It's all for one and one for all,
Pass and move, we're talking Total Football.
Here we go again, Roy's red machine,
Liverpool the greatest team the world has ever
seen.

[Chorus]:
Pass and move, it's the Liverpool groove,
Pass and move, it's the Liverpool groove,
Pass and move, pass and move, pass and move,
pass and move,

Pass and move, it's the Liverpool groove.
Pass and move, it's the Liverpool groove,
Pass and move, it's the Liverpool groove,
Pass and move, pass and move, pass and move,
pass and move,
Pass and move, it's the Liverpool groove.

Go Robbie, go Robbie, go,
Go Robbie, go Robbie, go,
Go Robbie, go Robbie, go,
Go Robbie, go Robbie, go.

Ho shimmy, shimmy, Stevie take it away,
Shaggy's in flight, now it's judgement day.
Digger in the middle, weaving his spell,
Jason McAteer like a bat outta hell.
R-r-red alert, Redknapp in attack,
Jamie's got the look, Jamie's got the mack.
Collymore in overdrive, ain't seen nothing yet,
Stanley on the goods, but God will bust the net.

Pass and move, it's the Liverpool groove,
Pass and move, it's the Liverpool groove,
Pass and move, pass and move, pass and move,
pass and move,
Pass and move, it's the Liverpool groove.

Go Robbie, go Robbie, go,
Go Robbie, go Robbie, go,
Go Robbie, go Robbie, go,
Go Robbie, go Robbie, go.
Go Robbie, go Robbie, go,
Go Robbie, go Robbie, go,
Go Robbie, go Robbie, go,
Go Robbie, go Robbie, go.

Scousers here, scousers there,
Scousers every...La la la la la la la.

Pass and move, it's the Liverpool groove,
Pass and move, it's the Liverpool groove,
Pass and move, pass and move, pass and move, pass and move,
Pass and move, it's the Liverpool groove.

Rushie's scored more than all the rest,
Respect to the lad with red upon his chest.
You get cut playing with the Razor,
Sharp like Armani, Jamo is the saviour.

Go Jamo, go Jamo, go,
Go Trigger, go Trigger, go,
Go Macca, go Macca, go,
Go Wrighty, go Wrighty, go,
Go Scalesy, go Scalesy, go,
Go Razor, go Razor, go,
Go Babbsy, go Babbsy, go,
Go Digger, go Digger, go,
Go Tommo, go Tommo, go,
Go Jamie, go Jamie, go,
Go Shaggy, go Shaggy, go,
Go Rushie, go Rushie, go,
Go Stanley, go Stanley, go.
Go Robbie, go Robbie, go,
Go Robbie, go Robbie, go,
Go Robbie, go Robbie, go.

Pass and move, it's the Liverpool groove,
Pass and move, it's the Liverpool groove,
It's the Liverpool groove.

(Another infamous recording from the Redmen as this official 1996
FA Cup anthem reached number four in the UK charts)

Patrik Berger
(To the tune of 'Lola' by The Kinks)

He's got long hair and he's strong as an ox,
And he scores great goals from the edge of the box,
His name is Berger,
La la, Patrik Berger.

Pepe Reina!

Pepe Reina, Pepe Reina, ay, ay!
Pepe Reina, Pepe Reina, ay, ay!

(The original and most common chant for our Spanish shot-stopper)

Phil Babb
(To the Match Of The Day theme tune)

Phil Babb Babb Babb Babb Babb Babb Babb Babb,
Phil Babb Babb Babb Babb Babb,
Phil Babb, Babb, Babb, Babb, Babb Babb Babb Babb,
Phil Babb Babb Babb Babb Babb,
Phil Babb Babb, Babb, Babb, Babb Babb Babb Babb,
Phil Babb Babb Babb Babb Babb,
Phil Babb Babb Babb Babb Babb Babb Babb Babb
Babb, Phil Babb Babb Babb Babb Babb Babb,
Phil Babb Phil Babb Phil Babb Phil Babb Babb!

*(Possibly the longest Liverpool song containing the fewest words,
but nevertheless this homage to our former Irish international
full-back is just as effective)*

Poor Scouser Tommy

One of the earliest and most defining Liverpool songs that has evolved alongside the club's success. The story is about a young Scouser who's sent off to fight in the war, but is shot down, and with his last breath he utters the verse that begins with 'oh I am a Liverpudlian'. First sung on the Kop during the '60s, it was updated in 1982 when Ian Rush put four past Everton in a 5-0 win at Goodison and was given a verse of his own. There remains some debate about the exact lyrics. For example some fans prefer to use the original "Libyan" or "radiant" sun instead of the more popular "Arabian" sun.

Poor Scouser Tommy

(To the tune of: 1st part – Red River Valley, 2nd part – The Sash,
3rd part – All You Need Is Love)

Let me tell you the story of a poor boy,
Who was sent far away from his home,
To fight for his king and his country,
And also the old folks back home.

So they put him in a Highland division,
Sent him off to a far foreign land,
Where the flies swarm around in their thousands,
And there's nothing to see but the sand.

Now the battle it started next morning,
Under the Arabian sun,
I remember that poor Scouser Tommy,
He was shot by an old Nazi gun.

As he lay on the battlefield dying, dying, dying,
With the blood gushing out of his head
(of his head),
As he lay on the battlefield dying, dying, dying,
These were the last words he said...

Oh I am a Liverpudlian,
And I come from the Spion Kop,
I like to sing, I like to shout,
I get thrown out quite a lot (every week).

I support a team that's dressed in red,
It's a team that you all know,
A team that we call LIVERPOOL,
To glory we will go.

We've won the League, we've won the Cup,
And we've been to Europe too,
We played the Toffees for a laugh and we left
'em feeling blue – Five Nil!

One, two,
One, two, three,
One, two, three, four,
Five-nil!

Rush scored one,
Rush scored two,
Rush scored three,
And Rush scored four,
Nah nah nah na nah nah nah nah.

All You Need Is Rush, nah nah nah nah nah,
All You Need Is Rush, nah nah nah nah nah,
All You Need Is Rush, Rush,
Rush Is All You Need.

Put Your Hands Up For Dirk Kuyt
(To the tune of 'Put Your Hands Up For Detroit'
by Fedde le Grand)

Put your hands up for up for Dirk Kuyt,
He loves this city.

(Voted in BBC Sports' top 10 football chants of 2006)

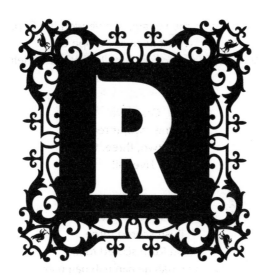

Rafa In Istanbul
(To the tune of 'Ghost Riders In The Sky' by Johnny Cash)

Mourinho said don't worry,
Chelsea have nothing to fear,
But how he went so quiet,
When up popped Luis Garcia.
His shot it had no power,
But then he took his goal,
And now he's taking Rafa to Istanbul.

[Chorus]:
Rafael, Rafael,
Rafa in Istanbul.

Benitez said don't worry,
I'll wipe away your tears,

'Cos Stevie G's a Red,
And a Red he'll be for years.
You can keep your John Terry,
Stick your Lampard up your ****,
'Cos Carragher is here,
And Gerrard's staying ours.

Rafael, Rafael,
Rafa in Istanbul.

*(Liverpool savour their 2005 Champions League semi-final
victory over Chelsea in song as they march on towards an
even bigger European night)*

Rafa, Rafael

*(To the tune of the famous old American frontier folk song
and children's favourite 'Skip To My Lou')*

We've got,
A coach from Spain,
He will,
Make us great again,
That is why,
We sing his name,
Rafael Benitez.

[Chorus]:
Rafa, Rafael,
Rafa, Rafael,
Rafa, Rafael,
Rafael Benitez.

*(Although the opening verse of this song is often dropped,
the chorus has become synonymous with Liverpool's
former Spanish manager)*

Rafa's Got His Dirk Out

Rafa's got his Dirk out,
Rafa's got his Dirk out,
Nah nah nah nah nah, Oi!!
Nah nah nah nah nah, Oi!!

(Commonly sung when the flying Dutchman was warming up on the sidelines during the Benitez era. It was most popular with supporters in Athens for the 2007 Champions League final)

Raul The Red

(To the nursery tune Row, Row, Row Your Boat)

Raul, Raul, Raul the Red,
Bald and Portuguese,
Meireles, Meireles, Meireles, Meireles,
Score a goal for me.

(This song emerged after Raul Meireles had scored his first Liverpool goal during the 2-2 Merseyside derby draw with Everton at Anfield in January 2011)

Red And White Kop

(To the tune of The Beatle's 'Yellow Submarine')

On a Saturday afternoon,
We support a team called Liverpool.
And we sing until we drop,
In a red and white Spion Kop
(Spion Kop!).

[Chorus]:
We all live in a red and white Kop,
A red and white Kop, a red and white Kop.
{Repeat}

In a town where I was born,
Lived a man who sailed the seas.
And he told me of his pride,
They were a famous football team.
So we trailed to Anfield Road,
Singing songs of victory.
And there we found the holy ground,
Of our hero Bill Shankly.

We all live in a red and white Kop,
A red and white Kop, a red and white Kop.
{Repeat}

(Another fans' favourite, although some prefer to sing: "On the famous Spion Kop" to "In a red and white Spion Kop")

Reds Never Tire
(To the tune of 'Mull of Kintyre' by Paul McCartney and The Wings)

Far have I travelled,
And much have I seen,
The years spent in Europe,
Now number twenty.
While all those around us,
All fade and they tire,
You will hear the Kop singing,
The Reds never tire.

[Chorus]:
The Reds never tire,

You'll hear the Kop singing,
You'll play with the fire,
That just keeps us winning,
The Reds never tire.

Now Everton are finished,
And Leeds they are dead,
Benfica and Gladbach,
Their faces are red.
The Cockneys are bottom,
They won't get much higher,
But you'll hear the Kop singing,
The Reds never tire.

The Reds never tire,
You'll hear the Kop singing,
You'll play with the fire,
That just keeps us winning,
The Reds never tire.

Now back in the sixties,
There's Hunt and St John,
With Steveo and Rowdy,
But sadly they're gone.
Today we've got Michael,
And Robbie on fire,
And you'll hear the Kop singing,
The Reds never tire.

The Reds never tire,
You'll hear the Kop singing,
You'll play with the fire,
That just keeps us winning,
The Reds never tire.

Ring Of Fire

The song synonymous with Istanbul and Liverpool's fifth European Cup. Although most fans are now familiar with the full lyrics, it's actually the instrumental interlude that gets sung. It was supposedly bellowed out by travelling Kopites as early as 2002 but came to prominence during the 2005 Champions League campaign – making Johnny Cash a household name again, two years after his death. Such was its roaring success, the club adopted it as their 2006 FA Cup anthem and was recorded by the newly-formed Boot Room All-Stars (Tim Speed and Apollo 440), and featured the vocals of lifelong Red and Echo And The Bunnymen frontman Ian McCulloch. It also contained backing vocals from travelling Reds at Old Trafford during the 2006 FA Cup semi-final victory over Chelsea and also the Kop during the final Premier League game of that season against Aston Villa.

Ring Of Fire

(To the tune of 'Ring Of Fire' by Johnny Cash)

Der-der-der-der-der-der-der-derrrrrr,
Der-der-der-der-der-der-der-derrrrrr,

Der-der-der-der-der-der-der-derrrrrr,
Der-der-der-der-der-der-der-derrrrrr.

[Repeat ad inifinitum]:

(Ring Of Fire was played in the Reds' dressing room ahead of the 2005 Champions League final. Steven Gerrard and Jamie Carragher were later seen on television singing the instrumental interlude during the post-match celebrations)

Robbie Fowler

(To the tune of 'That's Amore' by Dean Martin)

When the ball hits the net,
It's a fairly safe bet that it's Fowler,
Robbie Fowler.

And when Liverpool score,
You will hear the Kop roar:
"Oh, it's Fowler,
Robbie Fowler."

Ian Rush, Roger Hunt,
Who's the best man up front?
Oh, it's Fowler,
Robbie Fowler.

He's the King of the Kop,
He's the best of the lot,
Robbie Fowler.

Robbie Keane

(To the tune of The Beatles' 'Let it Be')

Robbie Keane, Robbie Keane,
Robbie Keane, Robbie Keane,
His name's not ******* Keano,
Robbie Keane.

*(This was sung by the Kop in 2008/09 in response
to Liverpool fans in the Main Stand chanting 'Keano, Keano'
– the Man United chant for Roy Keane – after Robbie
had scored for the Reds)*

Rockin' Around With Stevie G
*(To the tune of Brenda Lee's 'Rockin Around
The Christmas Tree')*

Rockin' around with Stevie G,
As he takes us to the top,
Singing a song for LFC,
On the famous Anfield Kop.

Rockin' around with Stevie G,
There's Riera on the wing.
Later you'll hear the fans all cheer,
When Fernando puts one in.

You will get a sentimental feeling when you hear,
Scousers singing: "Let's be jolly,
Pepe Reina is our goalie."

Rockin' around with Stevie G,
See the happy Kopites sway.
Everyone dancing merrily,
In the new old-fashioned way.

Roma

(To the tune 'Arrivederci Roma')

We're on our way to Roma,
On the 25th of May.
All the Kopites will be singing,
Vatican Bells they will be ringing,
Liverpool boys they will be drinking,
When we win the European Cup.
We'll be drinking all their vino,
On the 23rd, 24th, 25th, 26th of May.
All the Kopites will be singing,
Vatican Bells they will be ringing,
Liverpool boys they will be drinking,
When we win the European Cup.

Now we went back to Roma,
On the 30th of May.
All the Kopites they were singing,
Vatican bells they were ringing,
Liverpool FC they were a swinging,
When we won the European Cup.

Romeo And Juliet

(Inspired by the prologue to Shakespeare's
'Romeo And Juliet')

[Chorus]:
Two clubs alike in dignity,
In Liverpool where we set our scene,
And Juliet's dad was Everton mad,
While Romeo's followed Bill Shankly's team.

As she was going to Goodison Park,
It being on derby day,
He passed her on his way to the match,
And pretended he'd lost his way.
'Ello dear Jill can you help me,
I'm sweating cobs 'cos it's ten to three,
If I don't find that Goodison Road,
I'm bound to miss Hunt's opening goal."

Two clubs alike in dignity,
In Liverpool where we set our scene,
And Juliet's dad was Everton mad,
While Romeo's followed Bill Shankly's team.

She flashed her saucy eyes at him,
And, oh, but they were Kendall-blue,
She answered him quite modestly,
"I'd rather be dead than a Red like you,
I'm a Catterick maverick through and through,
And I would die for the lads in Blue,
But I'll guide you to the holy ground,
Lest you miss Alan scoring two."

Two clubs alike in dignity,
In Liverpool where we set our scene,
And Juliet's dad was Everton mad,
While Romeo's followed Bill Shankly's team.

He arched his back against the bar,
To save her from the swaying fans,
They sang 'You'll Never Walk Alone',
And they left Goodison hand in hand.
Well Juliet's dad went raving mad,
And Romeo's nearly went berserk,
But over a black-and-tan that night,
They agreed mixed marriages never work.
So while the moon was shining bright,
Our star-struck lovers eloped one night,
On the midnight ferry they crossed over,
Now they're both supporting Tranmere Rovers.

Two clubs alike in dignity,
In Liverpool where we set our scene,
And Juliet's dad was Everton mad,
While Romeo's followed Bill Shankly's team.

(The intense rivalry between the blue and red half of
Liverpool is cast aside in this amusing and artistic
interpretation of a famous playwright's work)

Said Bertie Mee

Said Bertie Mee,
To Bill Shankly:
"Have you heard of the North Bank, Highbury?"
Shanks said: "No, I don't think so,
But I've heard of the Anny Road aggro."

*(Sung by Road Enders and takes the form of a dialogue
between Shanks and former Arsenal boss Bertie Mee.
Similar to 'The Na Na Na Song')*

Sami Hyypia
(To 'The Addams Family' theme tune)

In our defensive foursome,
He's massive and he's awesome,
From corners he will score some,
He's Sami Hyypia.

Scouser In Gay Paree

(To the tune of 'Under The Bridges Of Paris' recorded by Eartha Kitt and Dean Martin)

[Chorus]:
How would you like to be,
A Scouser in Gay Paree,
Walking along on the banks of the Seine,
Winning the European Cup once again.

We'll go up the Eiffel Tower,
And stay up there half an hour,
'Cos we won't be too late,
When we celebrate,
We're the Scousers in Gay Paree.

We'll visit the Follies Bergere,
They like to see Scousers there,
The woman are lovely,
With skin like a peach,
But they'll never move it like Kenny Dalglish.

How would you like to be,
A Scouser in Gay Paree,
Walking along on the banks of the Seine,
Winning the European Cup once again.

(Written by a group of Reds from the Canon Pub in Townsend Lane, this is one of several marching songs for supporters making their way to the French capital to witness the European Cup final victory over Real Madrid in 1981. Fans also repeatedly chanted "Gay Paree" to the 'Ere we go' mantra, while the famous 'Tell Me Ma' song was given an overhaul for the occasion, as fans sent instructions back home "that we won't be home for tea, we're going to Gay Paree" It was also revived for the 1997 Cup Winners' Cup semi-final against PSG)

Scousers Rule
(To the tune 'Don't You Forget It' by Perry Como)

Scousers rule, and don't you forget it,
Scousers rule, and don't you forget it,
Scousers rule, and don't you forget it,
Chel-sea.

Shankly's Dream

There are many who doubt we existed,
Years ago, years ago,
But they tended to be bitter and he twisted,
Like Big Joe, like Big Joe.
But we'd won five league trophies before Shanks had come,
We had players like Liddell and Scott.
We're the boys from the Kop,
Liverpool is our team,
And Houllier's reliving Shankly's dream.

We got blessed by a great man of vision,
Bill Shankly, Bill Shankly.
And he led us out the Second Division,
We thank thee, we thank thee.
Then we won every trophy that football has seen,
'This Is Anfield' was known throughout the land.
We're the boys from the Kop,
Liverpool is our team,
And Houllier's reliving Shankly's dream.

Everybody in the world heard us singing,

From our ground, from our ground.
And they copied us from Mancland to Peking,
Mersey Sound, Mersey Sound.
Then the players would turn up and we'd make them laugh,
Gordon Banks, Franny Lee and Big Jack.
We're the boys from the Kop,
Liverpool is our team,
And Houllier's reliving Shankly's dream.

Then Bob Paisley he did even better,
Than Shankly, than Shankly.
Euro Cups in a cardie, trendsetter,
He won three, he won three.
He was shy, he was quiet but by God he was great,
And we loved him just like we loved Shanks.
We're the boys from the Kop,
Liverpool is our team,
And Houllier's reliving Shankly's dream.

Then came Heysel and Kenny took over,
From old Joe, from old Joe.
For a while we were rolling in clover,
Watch us go, watch us go.
And he won us the double against Everton,
Wembley sounded like never before.
We're the boys from the Kop,
Liverpool is our team,
And Houllier's reliving Shankly's dream.

We were shocked, we were stunned, we were shaken,
When it came, when it came.
All those children of Shanks that were taken,
At a game, just a game.
And we'll never forget them as long as we live,

They are with us now like they were then.
We're the boys from the Kop,
Liverpool is our team,
And Houllier's reliving Shankly's dream.

Came a decade that kept us all waiting,
For a team, for a team.
And now Gerard has started creating,
Our new dream, our new dream.
And deep down inside us, we all do believe,
That he'll take us back where we belong.
We're the boys from the Kop,
Liverpool is our team,
And Houllier's reliving Shankly's dream.

*(Fans mark the club's journey since the days of Shankly as the
achievements of successive managers are marked in melody)*

Show Them
(To the folk tune "Show Me The Way To Go Home')

Show them the way to go home,
They're tired and they want to go to bed,
'Cos they're only half a football team,
Compared to the boys in Red, Oi!

Side By Side
*(To the tune 'Side By Side' recorded by Brenda Lee, Dean Martin
and Frankie Laine among others)*

Oh we've no longer Shankly and Paisley,

Or a horse that is gangly and crazy,
But we've Thommo and Ged,
Wearing the Red,
Side by side.

Oh we're leaving the nineties behind us,
In Dortmund is where you will find us,
Wearing the Red,
With Thommo and Ged,
Side by side.

They'll win many trophies,
Just you wait and see,
Just like Shanks, Bob, Joe and Kenny,
They will win more than three.

So we're leaving the nineties behind us,
In Europe is where you will find us,
Just wearing the Red,
With Thommo and Ged,
SIDE BY SIDE

*(Created for the managerial partnership of Gerard Houllier
and Phil Thompson ahead of the Reds' 2001 UEFA Cup final
appearance in Dortmund)*

Sitting On Top Of The World

[Chorus]:
We're all sitting on top,
Sitting on top of the world.
The team that no-one can stop,
We're sitting on top of the world.

Liverpool, Liverpool,
Proud to call your name.
You touched our heart,
And now we're part of Liverpool.
Oh how we love to sing:

Liverpool, Liverpool
We'll always follow you.
Through thick and thin,
We know we'll win,
And make your dreams come true.

We're all sitting on top,
Sitting on top of the world.
The team that no-one can stop,
We're sitting on top of the world.

Liverpool, Liverpool,
Always by your side.
With love so strong,
We can't go wrong,
We're Liverpool.
Oh how we love to sing:

Liverpool, Liverpool,
Winners all the way.
When we walk up,
To lift the cup,
We'll hold it high and say:

We're all sitting on top,
Sitting on top of the world.
The team that no-one can stop,
We're sitting on top of the world.

Ooooh wooooah, oooooh wooooah.
Li-ver-poool, Li-ver-poool.

We're all sitting on top,
Sitting on top of the world.
Team that no-one can stop,
We're sitting on top of the world.

We're all sitting on top,
Sitting on top of the world.
The team that no-one can stop,
We're sitting on top,
We're sitting on top,
We're sitting on top of the world.

(The official club anthem to the 1986 all-Merseyside
FA Cup final, reaching number 50 in the UK charts)

Spackman
(To the Batman theme tune)

Ner-ner, ner-ner, ner-ner, ner-ner,
Ner-ner, ner-ner, ner-ner, ner-ner,
Spackman!

SpAnfield Rap
(To the tune 'Anfield Rap' by the Liverpool FA Cup
final squad of 1988)

Liverpool FC is hard as hell,
Chavski, Man Ure, Arsenal.
Watch my lips 'cos I will spell,

That they're not just Scouse,
But they're Spanish as well.

Liverpool FC,
Liverpool FC.

(We control the game, we play a high tempo and at
the end the most important thing is we win…)

Never call me the special one!

[Chorus]:
*Walk on…walk on…with hope…in your heart…and
you'll ne…ver walk…alone.*

Alright Carra?
Just chucked a pound,
Jose wants me,
But I'm not goin' down.
The rest of the lads,
Ain't speaking Scouse,
And none of 'em live in a Robbie house.

Well I'm singing now, 'cos we've won five,
I'm your goalie, number 25,
I like to punch, don't call me a clown,
Or like Arjen Robben, you're going down.
Didi's ace, he's like me and you,
He wears shell-suits and likes the Grafton too.
But the rest aren't like us, are they doh la,
We'll have to teach 'em to rob a car.

*Walk on…walk on…with hope…in your heart…and
you'll ne…ver walk…alone.*

You two Scousers are always yapping,
Like that kid I'll give you both a slapping.
I come from Auxerre, my name is Djibril,
And when I spin my decks the dancefloors fill.

Howz he a DJ when he says he's French?
He gets time to practice when he's sat on the bench.
He gives us stick but he's not in the side,
He can't play up front,
So he plays out wide.

Well I came to Anfield not wanting to fail,
But I got injured and grew a pony-tail.
Now I'm back on the left, in the form of my life,
And I've got a peachy arse, according to my wife.

They've won it five times, three more than Man U,
They think they're great, but they've only ever won two.
No one knows quite what to expect,
When Rafa says who's playing next.

Well Mourinho sure is bitter,
And the more he moans, the more we titter.
He can't win a semi, against the Redmen,
And now he needs, Just for Men.
Just4men… Just4men… Just4men… Just4men.
Liverpool FC is hard as hell.

(We control the game, we play a high tempo and at
the end the most important thing is we win…)

Never call me the special one!

We're Spanish lads,
Hola to you,
And there's four of us,
And only two of you.
So please talk more slowly,
And get us el beer,
We'll have three Sols, Luis wants Sangria.

Don't forget big Sami,
And Momo came from Spain,
I'm six-foot seven boys so watch your game.
You two Scousers, you're always squawking,
Riise just lets his Mum do the talking.

Our lads come from all over the place,
Finn's a Cockney Paddy and Jerzy's lost his
place.
Well now we gotta learn 'em to talk real sound,
And sing to Ring of Fire as we dance round the
ground.

Der der-der der der der derrrrr,
Der der-der, der der der derrrrr.

Ho-ho my word,
That's unbelievable, it really is.
I think they should stick to playing football.
Terrible.
What do you think Rafa?

We controlled the game....

(Written by Chris McLoughlin, this was The Kop Magazine's
May 2006 parody of the Anfield Rap ahead of the FA Cup
final against West Ham)

Ste Gerrard
(To the tune 'Que Sera Sera')

Ste Gerrard, Gerrard,
Can pass the ball 40 yards,
He's big and he's ******* hard,
Ste Gerrard, Gerrard.

Ste Gerrard, Gerrard,
Can pass the ball 40 yards,
He's better than Frank Lampard,
Ste Gerrard, Gerrard.

Steve Finnan
(To the children's song 'Michael Finnegan')

We've got a right-back called Steve Finnan,
When he plays we're always winnin',
Passes the ball,
Out and in again,
We've got a right-back called Steve Finnan.

Steve Heighway
(To the tune 'My Way' by Frank Sinatra)

My Friends, the time has come
To tell you of our new sensation.
A man we got from Skem,
At him we look with great elation.
We watch his magic course,

Down either wing, along the by-way,
And soon, the world will know,
His name is Heighway.

Sometimes he's immature,
When on the wing or in the middle,
But with a heart like Hunt's,
The strength and speed of Billy Liddell.
He's got all St. John's class,
And they're the best I've seen in my day,
But more, much more than this,
Has Stevie Heighway.

Who is this man, where is he from?
Defenders ask: "Where has he gone?"
He fools them all,
There is no doubt,
This is the man this song's about,
And like the Kop,
You'll hear me shout:
"Give it to Heighway."

My friends the time has come,
When we must find another scorer.
For now that Roger's gone,
I'll tell you friends there's nothing surer.
He played with all his heart,
And gave all he had along the by-way,
And now that he is gone,
We've Steve Heighway.

At times he didn't score,
But they were times,
Too few to mention.
300 goals or more,

He scored with one intention,
To please the crowd he loved.
And took the praise in such a shy way,
And now that he is gone.
We've Steve Heighway.

Yes, there were times,
I thought he knew,
When he bit off more than he could chew.
He didn't know the word defeat,
He used his head,
He used his feet.
The record stands, it's in the hands,
Of Stevie Heighway.

Stevie G (I)
(To the tune '99 Red Balloons' by Nena)

Stevie Gerrard for the 'Pool,
Stevie G for the 'Pool,
Stevie Gerrard, Stevie G,
Stevie score a goal for me.

You'll hear this song echo around,
From all four corners of the ground.
He hits the net from 40 yards,
Euro glories on the cards.

With Stevie G and Gary Mac,
The glory days are coming back.
And Gerard Houllier's on the line,
As 96 red balloons fly by.
Nananananananana

Stevie G (II)

(To the tune 'Let It Be' by the Beatles)

When we find ourselves in times of trouble,
Stevie G runs past me,
Playing the game with wisdom,
Stevie G.

And in my home, the Spion Kop,
We watch him jog, right in front of me,
Spreading balls with wisdom,
Stevie G.

[Chorus]:
Let it be, let it be,
Let it be, Stevie G,
The local lad turned hero,
Stevie G.

And when the jubilant Kopite people,
All living in The Park agree,
That we all know the answer,
Stevie G.

And although we may all be fooled,
There is still a chance that we will see,
The footballing phenomenon,
Stevie G.

Let it be, let it be,
Let it be, Stevie G,
Spreading balls with wisdom,
Stevie G.

And when the night is cloudy,
There is still a man that we all see,
A young, committed Kopite,
Stevie G.

Playing to the sound of music,
Stevie G runs past me,
Playing the game with wisdom,
Stevie G.

Let it be, let it be,
Let it be, Stevie G,
For we all know the answer,
His name is Stevie G.

Steven Gerrard Is Our Captain

(To the tune of 'Tin Whistle' from the Robin Hood
animated movie)

Steven Gerrard is our captain,
Steven Gerrard is a Red,
Steven Gerrard plays for Liverpool,
A Scouser born and bred.

Deh deh deh deh deh deh...
Deh deh deh deh deh deh...
Deh deh deh deh deh deh...
Deh deh deh deh deh deh...

And then one night in Turkey,
It was 21 years since Rome,
With a Liverbird upon his chest,
He brought the cup back home.

Super Dan
(To the nursery folk song 'Bobby Shafto's Gone To Sea)

Super, super Dan,
Super, super Dan,
Super, super Dan,
Super Danny Murphy.

(After scoring some big goals in big games during his time with the Reds, it was only natural fans' favourite Danny Murphy should be honoured with his own tune)

SuperCroatIgorBiscan
(To the 'Supercalifragilisticexpialidocious' tune from Mary Poppins)

SuperCroatIgorBiscan used to be atrocious,
Used to playing at the back,
And driving his Ford Focus.
Now he's turned into a swan and not a diplodocus,
SuperCroatIgorBiscan used to be atrocious.

Sweet Sixteen
(To the tune 'You're Sixteen, You're Beautiful' by Ringo Starr)

We went down to the Bridge,
We needed a win,
And King Kenny stuck the ball in the net,
It's sixteen,
It's beautiful and it's mine.

Team Of Carraghers

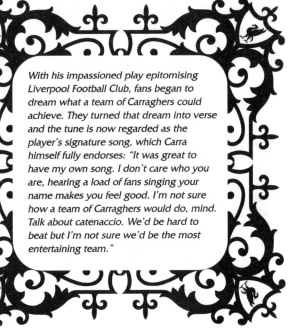

With his impassioned play epitomising Liverpool Football Club, fans began to dream what a team of Carraghers could achieve. They turned that dream into verse and the tune is now regarded as the player's signature song, which Carra himself fully endorses: "It was great to have my own song. I don't care who you are, hearing a load of fans singing your name makes you feel good. I'm not sure how a team of Carraghers would do, mind. Talk about catenaccio. We'd be hard to beat but I'm not sure we'd be the most entertaining team."

Team Of Carraghers

(To the tune 'Yellow Submarine' by The Beatles)

[Chorus]:
We all dream of a team of Carraghers,
A team of Carraghers,
A team of Carraghers.
We all dream of a team of Carraghers,
A team of Carraghers,
A team of Carraghers.

Number one is Carragher,
Number two is Carragher,
Number three is Carragher,
Number four is Carragher......

We all dream of a team of Carraghers,
A team of Carraghers,
A team of Carraghers.
We all dream of a team of Carraghers,
A team of Carraghers,
A team of Carraghers.

Number five is Carragher,
Number six is Carragher,
Number seven is Carragher,
Number eight is Carragher......

We all dream of a team of Carraghers,
A team of Carraghers,
A team of Carraghers.
We all dream of a team of Carraghers,
A team of Carraghers,
A team of Carraghers.

Number nine is Carragher,
Number ten is Carragher,
Number eleven is Carragher,
Number twelve is Carragher......

We all dream of a team of Carraghers,
A team of Carraghers,
A team of Carraghers.
We all dream of a team of Carraghers,
A team of Carraghers,
A team of Carraghers.

Number thirteen is Carragher,
Number fourteen is Carragher,
Number fifteen is Carragher,
Number twenty-three is Carragher......

We all dream of a team of Carraghers,
A team of Carraghers,
A team of Carraghers.
We all dream of a team of Carraghers,
A team of Carraghers,
A team of Carraghers.

Teddy Bears' Piechnik

(To the tune 'Teddy Bears' Picnic)

Der der da der der da der der der, der der da
der der der,
Der der da der der da der der der, der der da
der der der,
Der der da der der da der der dah,
Der der da der der da der der dah,
Der der da da der der da Torben Piechnik!

*(Our former Danish defender gets the pay-off line to a
children's classic)*

Tell Me Ma

(To the tune 'Que Sera Sera')

Tell me Ma, me Ma,
I don't want no tea, no tea,
We're going to Italy,
Tell me Ma, me Ma.

[Alternative version]:

Tell me Ma, me Ma,
That I won't be home for tea,
We're going to Gay Paree,
Tell me Ma, me Ma.

[Alternative version]:

Tell me Ma, me Ma,
I don't want no tea, no tea,

We're going to Germany,
Tell me Ma, me Ma.

[Alternative version]:

Tell me Ma, me Ma,
To put the Champagne on ice,
We're going to Cardiff twice,
Tell me Ma, me Ma.

[Alternative version]:

Tell me Ma, me Ma
I don't want no bacon barms,
I'm going to Cardiff Arms,
Tell me Ma, me Ma.

*(Original version first heard in 1977 when Liverpool set
about winning the European Cup in Rome and then adapted
it for other significant cup finals including Paris '81,
Dortmund 2001, and the back-to-back appearances at the
Millennium Stadium in 2001)*

Thanks To The Shanks

He was born in bonny Scotland,
And he played the football game,
He came to Liverpool in '59,
To help us win again.
Then with his mighty Red army,
He marched to victory,
He was a legend in his time.
Our hero Bill Shankly.

[Chorus]:
So all say thanks to the Shanks,
He never walked alone,
Let's sing our song for all the world,
From this his Liverpool home.

No matter were you come from,
No matter who you are,
Remember the year of '59,
When the Reds they found a star.
And now he shines so brightly,
For the boys of Liverpool,
Soon the world was about to find,
This man was nobody's fool.

So all say thanks to the Shanks,
He never walked alone.
Let's sing our song for all the world,
From this his Liverpool home.

Then he asked no favours,
Just hard work, let's get it right,
You can only succeed through dedication,
And his men they all saw the light.
He gave this town his loyalty,
And proved it all by success,
So always remember when we had Bill Shankly,
We all knew we had the best.

So all say thanks to the Shanks,
He never walked alone.
Let's sing our song for all the world,
From this his Liverpool home.

That Night In Istanbul

(To the tune of 'The Night Chicago Died' by Paper Lace)

In the heat of a Turkish night,
By half-time we were down three-nil,
But the spirit never died,
People talk about it still.

Milan had us on the run,
Others thought that we were done,
But you could hear the Kopites shout,
We may be down but we're not out.

[Chorus]:
That night in Istanbul,
We saw the spirit that is Liverpool,
Brother what a night the people saw,
What a fightback the people saw,
Mercy me.

That night they played with pride,
With heart and soul that cannot be denied.
They gave their all and so much more,
Like all those glory days before,
Yes indeed.

Stevie G got us back in the game,
With a goal that made us scream,
Smicer put away a second one,
Now it was time to live the dream.

When Alonso made it three,
With a double strike penalty,
Then the whole place came alive,
And by the end we made it FIVE.

That night they played with pride,
With heart and soul that cannot be denied.
They gave there all and so much more,
Like all those glory days before,
Yes indeed.

That night in Istanbul,
We saw the spirit that is Liverpool,
Brother what a night the people saw,
What a fightback the people saw,
Mercy me.

That night they played with pride,
With heart and soul that cannot be denied.
They gave there all and so much more,
Like all those glory days before,
Yes indeed.

(The never-say-die attitude of Liverpool's 2005 Champions
League final team is commemorated with an equally
spirited show of support from the Kop choir)

The Ballad Of Istanbul
(To the tune of 'The Ballad Of John And Yoko'
by The Beatles)

Waiting in the lounge at JLA,
Trying to get to Turkey to dance,
The newspaper hack said:
"You gotta go back,"
You know they didn't even give us a chance!

[Chorus]:
Christ, you know it ain't easy,

You know how hard it can be,
The way Liverpool are playing,
She's gonna crucify me.

Some lads got the flight in from Paris,
Some are flying in from Cologne.
Bulgaria's full,
And so's Istanbul,
'Cos the Redmen never walk alone!

Christ, you know it ain't easy,
You know how hard it can be,
The way Liverpool are playing,
She's gonna crucify me.

From Grazier to the Istanbul hostels,
Some lads are staying for a week.
The Major has said,
When the winners are Red,
We're all going to Japan on the cheap!

Christ, you know it ain't easy,
You know how hard it can be,
The way Liverpool are playing,
She's gonna crucify me.

When Carra brings the Cup back to Bootle,
We're all going on the ale for a week.
Rafa said to the hack,
"We're not giving it back,"
'Cos UEFA said we've got it for keeps!

(Also referred to as 'She's Gonna Crucify Me,' this song tells
the story of Istanbul from the fans' point of view as they
journeyed to the Ataturk)

The Best Centre Forward's Wearing Red

Oh, the best centre forward's wearing red,
He's wearing red,
Wearing red,
Wearing red, red, red.
Oh, the best centre forward's wearing red,
He's wearing red,
Wearing red,
Wearing red, red, red.
And every time he touches the ball he scores a goal,
Every time he touches the ball he scores a goal,
Every time he touches the ball he scores a goal,
He's Terry Mac,
Terry Mac,
Super Terry Mac.

Oh, the worst centre forward's wearing black,
He's wearing black,
Wearing black,
Wearing black, black, black.
Oh, the worst centre forward's wearing black
He's wearing black,
Wearing black,
Wearing black, black, black.
And every time he opens his mouth he swallows the ball,
Every time he opens his mouth he swallows the ball,
Every time he opens his mouth he swallows the ball,
He's Malcolm Mac,
Malcolm Mac,
Malcolm Mac, Mac, Mac.

(Reds champion their goalscoring hero Terry McDermott during the seventies while telling Newcastle fans exactly what they think of their own Mac – Malcom MacDonald)

The Boys Of LFC

(To the tune of 'I've Never Been To Me' by Charlene)

Oh we've been to Nice and we've been to
Greece,
And we've done the treble in Rome,
We've been to Moscow and Monte Carlo,
And never walked alone.
Oh we've been Europe's kings and we've seen
some things,
That a bluenose will never see,
We are the Spion Kop,
The Boys of LFC.

The Green, Green Grass Of Anfield

(To the tune of 'Green, Green Grass Of Home'
by Tom Jones)

The old Kop looks the same,
As I stepped down to watch the game,
There's the green, green grass that Liddell used
to play on,
Now there's Hunt, St John and Peter Thompson,
They score a goal when Shankly wants them,
It's good to watch the greatest team at home,
And we'll all be there to see big Rowdy,
And the team that serves us proudly,
When they bring the league championship back
home.

(Stars past and present get worthy mention in this
re-working of Tom Jones' hit which topped the UK
charts in 1966)

The Liverbird Of Liverpool FC
(To the folk song 'The Yellow Rose Of Texas')

Have you ever heard of the Liverbird of Liverpool FC?
Proud on the chest of the team that's best,
The team for you and me.
The team of Billy Liddell, Dalglish and Bill Shankly,
We'll fight, fight, fight, for the red and white of Liverpool FC.

The McAteer
(To 'The Macarena' by Los del Rio)

He flies down the wing and his name's McAteer,
He's from Birkenhead and he talks like a *****,
He cost four mill so he was pretty dear,
Hey McAteer!

The Men From Anfield's Spion Kop
(To the tune of 'The Shores Of Tripoli')

We are the men from Anfield's Spion Kop,
Our team is Liverpool FC.
We like to sing and shout,
Because we know,
We'll cheer the team to victory.
For it's a great team you'll agree,
And we'll go down in history.
We've won the cup, been champions too,
And today we'll murder you,
We're the Liverpool FC.

And if you go to any ground,
You'll always hear our songs.
To see our team we'll be there,
For we know our team will,
FIGHT, FIGHT, FIGHT,
It's gonna be a glorious,
SIGHT, SIGHT, SIGHT.

We all agree it's gonna be,
Another glorious victory,
For the Liverpool FC.

The Mo Mo Mo Song
(To the theme tune from kids' TV programme 'The Banana Splits')

Mo Mo Mo, Mo Sissoko, Mo Mo Mo, Mo Sissoko,
Mo Mo Mo, Mo Sissoko, Mo Mo Mo, Mo Sissoko.

The Monster Masch
(To the tune of 'Monster Mash' by Bobby Pickett)

I was working in Melwood late one night,
When my eyes beheld an eerie sight,
For Mascherano from his slab began to rise,
And suddenly to my surprise:

He did the Masch,
He did the monster Masch,
The monster Masch
It was an Anfield smash,
He did the Masch,

It caught on in a flash,
He did the Masch,
He did the monster Masch.

From my laboratory in Melwood east,
To the dressing room where the Skrtel feasts,
The players all came from their humble abodes,
To get a jolt from the Masch electrodes.

They did the Masch,
They did the monster Masch,
The monster Masch,
It was an Anfield smash,
They did the Masch,
It caught on in a flash,
They did the Masch,
They did the monster Masch.

The players were having fun,
The party had just begun,
The guests included Gerrard,
Carragher and his son.

The scene was rockin', all were digging the sounds,
Skrtel on chains, backed by his baying hounds,
The Kopites were about to arrive,
With their vocal group, 'The Anfield Rap Five.'

They played the Masch,
They played the monster Masch,
The monster Masch,
It was an Anfield smash,
They played the Masch,
It caught on in a flash,

They played the Masch,
They played the monster Masch.

Out from his office, Rafa's voice did ring,
Seems he was troubled by just one thing.
He opened the door and shook his fist,
And said, "Whatever happened to my
Mascherano twist?"

It's now the Masch,
It's now the monster Masch,
The monster Masch,
And it's an Anfield smash,
It's now the Masch,
It's caught on in a flash,
It's now the Masch,
It's now the monster Masch.

Now everything's cool, Stevie's part of the band,
And my monster Masch is the hit of the land.
For you, the Kopites, this Masch was meant to,
When you get to my door, tell them Rafa sent you.

Then you can Masch,
Then you can monster Masch,
The monster Masch,
And do my Anfield smash,
Then you can Masch,
You'll catch on in a flash,
Then you can Masch,
Then you can monster Masch.

*(An artistic interpretation of Billy Pickett's 1962 US chart
topper is afforded to El Jefecito during his three-year
spell at the club)*

The Music Man

*(Taken from the classic children's folksong 'The Music Man',
also recorded by Black Lace)*

He is the music man,
He comes from sunny Spain.
And he can play,
What is his name.
Xabi ...Alonso...

The Na Na Na Song

One fine day, my dad said to me,
Do you want to come the Kop and see the LFC?
I said: "No, I don't think so,
'Cos I'm going down the Anny Road for the aggro."

Na na na na na na na,
Na na na na na na na,
Na na na na na na na,
We are the Anny Road
AGGRO!

The One And Only Bill Shankly

*(To the tune of 'Sgt Pepper's Lonely Hearts Club Band'
by The Beatles)*

It was forty-five years ago today,
When great Bill Shankly taught the Reds to play.
He gave to us the passing style,

That was guaranteed to make us smile.
So let me introduce to you,
The man we've loved for all these years.
The one and only Bill Shankly....

The Pride Of Merseyside (I)
*(To the tune of 'Paloma Blanca' by Dutch band
George Baker Selection)*

When the ground is full of Kopites,
And the kick off time is near,
Here's the song we'll be singing,
When the boys in Red appear.

[Chorus]:
Liverpool are the greatest,
The greatest team in the land.
Liverpool have the greatest,
The greatest fans in the land.
We are the pride,
Of Merseyside.

Liverpool – they are pure magic,
And no matter where they play,
When we go all over Europe,
You can hear the people say...

Liverpool are the greatest,
The greatest team in the land.
Liverpool have the greatest,
The greatest fans in the land.
We are the pride,
Of Merseyside.

We'll collect another trophy,
When we go and play in Rome,
And all the Kopites will be singing,
When we're on our way back home.

Liverpool are the greatest,
The greatest team in the land.
Liverpool have the greatest,
The greatest fans in the land.
We are the pride,
Of Merseyside.

The Pride Of Merseyside (II)

No work, no hope, one chance for fame,
It's our life, not just a game.
For the Reds, grown men have cried,
They're the pride of Merseyside.

[Chorus]:
With Liverbirds upon their chest,
Liverpool, the world's best.
This great team trusted and tried,
They're the pride of Merseyside.

The angels came, took Shanks away,
And from above, we heard him say:
"Give me the men, whose hearts have bled,
Make them proud to wear the Red."

With Liverbirds upon their chest,
Liverpool, the world's best.

This great team trusted and tried,
They're the pride of Merseyside.

And now our glory will never stop,
We've got King Kenny,
We've got the Kop.
One thing we have, we'll never hide,
We're the pride of Merseyside.

With Liverbirds upon their chest,
Liverpool, the world's best.
This great team trusted and tried,
They're the pride of Merseyside.

The Scarf My Father Wore

(To the Irish ballad 'The Sash My Father Wore')

It was back in nineteen-sixty-five,
On the very first day of May,
Me Dad sang and danced for the lads in Red,
As he walked down Wembley Way.
Ian St. John scored the goal that won,
The Cup we'd never won before,
And as his son I love to wear,
The scarf my father wore.

It is old but it is beautiful,
And its colours they are fine,
It was worn in Paris, Wember-ly,
In Rome and on the Rhine.
My father wore it as a youth,
In the bygone days of yore,
And as his son I love to wear,
The scarf my father wore.

The Soldier Song
(To the chorus from the Irish national anthem – 'The Solider's Song')

Loyalists are we whose lives are pledged to Anfield,
We have come, (where from),
From the mighty Spion Kop.
Sworn to be Red, we're loyal Liverpudlians,
We'll follow our team throughout the land,
Tonight we'll raise the red flag high,
For Liverpool we live and die.
And as we march, eternal light,
We will chant a loyal song, Liverpool.

The Torres Bounce
(To the tune of 'When Johnny Comes Marching Home')

His armband proved he was a Red,
Torres, Torres,
'You'll Never Walk Alone' it said,
Torres, Torres.
We got the lad from sunny Spain,
He gets the ball, he scores again,
Fernando Torres, Liverpool's number nine!

[Bounce]
Na na, na na, na na, na na, na na, na nah,
Na na, na na, na na, na na, na na, na nah,
Na na, na na, na na, na nh, na na, na na, na na, na nah,
Fernando Torres, Liverpool's number nine!

*(Although no longer at the club, this song – also known as the
'Fernando Torres – Liverpool's Number Nine' tune – forms part of
the club's chanting history. Fans would warn of they're intentions
when opening with "We're gonna bounce in a minute")*

There's A Man From France
(To the French national anthem 'La Marseillaise')

There's a man from France that makes us dance,
His name is Gerard Houllier,
Gerard Houllier.
He's the best in the land by faaaaar,
His name is Gerard Houlliaaaaaa.

There's Only One Freddie Boswell

One Freddie Boswell,
There's only one Freddie Boswell,
One Freddie Boswell.

*(Sung to chairman David Moores when he opened the
Centenary Stand in 1992)*

These Reds Are Your Reds
(To the tune of Woody Guthrie's 'This Land Is Your Land')

[Chorus]:
These Reds are your Reds,
These Reds are my Reds.
From Bill Shankly, to Rafa Benitez;
From Robbie Fowler to Fernando Torres,
These Reds they play for you and me.

As I was sitting here in L4,
All around me I heard the Kop roar,

And below me I saw the Reds score,
These Reds they play for you and me.

In Rome they conquered and I followed their footsteps,
The crown they reclaimed in the Istanbul desert,
And all around me voices were sounding,
These Reds they play for you and me.

These Reds are your Reds,
These Reds are my Reds.
From Bill Shankly, to Rafa Benitez;
From Robbie Fowler to Fernando Torres,
These Reds they play for you and me.

When the sun comes shining, the boys are strolling,
And the grass is waving and the net keeps rolling,
As the cup is lifted and voices chanting,
These Reds they play for you and me.

The Reds will not yield as they see a proud sign,
And on the sign it says: "This Is Anfield,"
And on the other side the Kop is singing,
These Reds they play for you and me.

These Reds are your Reds,
These Reds are my Reds.
From Bill Shankly, to Rafa Benitez;
From Robbie Fowler to Fernando Torres,
These Reds they play for you and me.

In the seats around me I see my people,
And on the pitch I see my people,
As they keep winning, we stand singing,
These Reds they play for you and me.

Nobody living can ever stop us,
As we keep walking the glory highway,
Nobody living can ever make us turn back,
These Reds they play for you and me.

These Reds are your Reds,
These Reds are my Reds.
From Bill Shankly, to Rafa Benitez;
From Robbie Fowler to Fernando Torres,
These Reds they play for you and me.

This Could Be

(To the tune of 'Rotterdam' by the Beautiful South)

This could be Parc de Princes or Wem-ber-ley,
Liverpool or Rome.
And when we win in Rotterdam,
We'll bring the cup back home,
Bring the cup back home.

(Another rousing tune for European nights as the Reds seek to land
the Cup Winners' Cup during the 1996/97 season. It was the trip to
Parc de Princes which proved their undoing however. Unable to
overturn a 3-0 semi-final first leg deficit to Paris St Germain, the
Reds were denied a showpiece final against eventual winners
Barcelona in Rotterdam)

Times They Are a-Changin'

(To the tune of 'The Times They Are a-Changin' by Bob Dylan)

I've supported this team, through man and boy,
I've treasured their glories, like a favourite toy.

Yet in times recent passed, our mantle had gone,
To the theatre of a thousand prawn sarnies!
But their fun in the sun, has it now come and gone?
For the times they are-a-changin'

I've delighted when I sighted Dalglish pass to Rush,
I've marvelled at McMahon give the midfield the push.
The Grob at the back whilst Digger attacked,
The Championship never in doubt!
Those days long ago, are they coming back home?
For the times they are-a-changin'

Well off went King Kenny we bade him farewell,
Along came old Souness, he gave us sheer hell!
Dear Roy you could feel his team had no steel,
But a Frenchman lies waiting to heal it!
With style, respect, and time to reflect,
For the times they are-a-changin'

With a five-year plan and a warm gentle hand,
Our 'Kopite from France' has made us all dance.
Five trophies in six months you just can't believe,
Get the Brasso, the duster, and roll up your sleeves!
Monsieur Houllier, I bow, you're the toast of the town!
For the times they are-a-changin'

Then one of our heroes he walks right away,
Young Robbie Fowler a very sad day.
A very strange sight to see him in white,
But bring on the stars of Senegal!
With power and pace, and smiles on their faces!
For the times they are-a-changin'

We've a squad to be proud in this famous old ground,

Our manager and coaches the best all around.
Dignity, belief, commitment and class,
The Holy Grail – is it within our grasp?
Let the Reds out, let's all sing and shout,
For the times they are-a-changin'

I said let the Reds out,
Let's all sing and shout,
For the times they are-a-changin'

(Created by Kopites to mark the club's changing fortunes under Gerard Houllier)

Titi Camara

(To the nursery folk song 'Bobby Shafto's Gone To Sea)

Ti-ti, Ti-ti Ti,
Ti-ti, Ti-ti Ti,
Ti-ti, Ti-ti Ti,
Ti-ti Ti Camara

(The Guinean striker is recalled fondly in this simple chant, the format of which has been made famous by Super Danny Murphy among others, and now lends itself to the club's next hot prospect, Daniel Pacheco)

Tommy Mascherano

(To the tune of 'Don't Cry For Me Argentina' by Madonna)

Mascherano from Argentina,
The truth is he is a Scouser,
He hates United,

He hates the Blue*****,
His real name's Tommy,
Mascherano...

*(Before his move to Barcelona, our former Argentinian
hardman was given the forename of the original Anfield
Iron, Tommy Smith, in this Evita adaptation)*

Too Good To Be True
(To the tune of 'Can't Take My Eyes Off You' by Frankie Valli)

You're just too good to be Blue,
Can't take the ball off of you,
You've got a heavenly touch,
You pass like Souness to Rush,
And when we're all ****** in the bars,
We thank the Lord that you're ours,
You're just to good to be true,
Can't take the ball off of you.

Oh Steven, Steven, Steven Gerrard,
Oh Steven, Steven, Steven Gerrard,
Oh Steven, Steven, Steven Gerrard,
Oh Steven Steven Geeeer-raaaard.

Oh Steven Gerrard,
Because he hates Man U,
Oh Steven Gerrard,
He hates the Blue***** too,
Oh Steven Gerrard,
You're a Red through and through.

[Repeat last verse]

Twelve Days Of Christmas

The abridged version of the alternative Christmas classic. Fans with more wind in their lungs can go through the whole repertoire of the song, repeating each line, much like the traditional offering as they build up to the twelfth day. The legendary line-up comes from the club's hugely successful squad between 1982-1984.

Twelve Days Of Christmas
(To the festive tune of 'Twelve Days Of Christmas')

On the 12th day of Christmas my true love gave to me,
12 David Hodgson,
11 Graeme Souness,
10 Craig Johnston,
9 Ian Rush,
8 Sammy Lee,
7 Kenny Dalglish,
6 Alan Hansen,
5 Ronnie Whelan,
4 Mark Lawrenson,
3 Barney Rubble,
2 Philip Neal,
And Brucie in our goal.

Two Little Reds
(To the tune of 'Two Little Boys' by Rolf Harris)

Two young reds, both in their beds,
dreaming of Hunt and Yeats.
Next day in school, they'd both drool at these two football greats.
Saturday came, they both went the game,
Wembley in '65.
Liverpool scored, the crowd applaud,
and the lads both saw it live.

[Chorus]:
If you think that I'd let you see us, win the cup by yourself,
you're wrong.

I'm always there next to you,
when we sing our Liverpool song.
Our leader Shanks is our hero,
we'll walk on through the wind and rain.
And side by side we'll be standing,
when we win this trophy again.

Twelve months passed, Shanks had the cast,
to win again Division One.
Liverpool were, as strong as before,
with Cally; Milne; St John.
Chelsea came, story's the same,
win the league in front of the Kop.
Both lads cried, as they realised,
that we were the cream of the crop.

If you think that I'd let you see us,
win the cup by yourself, you're wrong.
I'm always there next to you,
when we sing our Liverpool song.
Our leader Shanks is our hero,
we'll walk on through the wind and rain.
And side by side we'll be standing,
when we win this trophy again.

In '73, the lads eagerly,
went to all the games that year.
Side by side, they'd not be defied,
as the Reds had no-one to fear.
The league came again, but used to it then,
they had a double within their sight.
Over the sea, and in Germany,
the UEFA Cup was won that night.

If you think that I'd let you see us,
win the cup by yourself, you're wrong.
I'm always there next to you,
when we sing our Liverpool song.
Our leader Shanks is our hero,
we'll walk on through the wind and rain.
And side by side we'll be standing,
when we win this trophy again.

Four years on, Shankly was gone,
but they'd seen more success with Bob.
The quiet man saw, what went before,
and he got right on with the job.
Now 23, and loyally,
both the lads made their way to Rome,
Smith and Neal, showed their appeal,
to bring the European Cup home.

If you think that I'd let you see us,
win the cup by yourself, you're wrong.
I'm always there next to you,
when we sing our Liverpool song.
Our leader Bob is our hero,
we'll walk on through the wind and rain.
And side by side we'll be standing,
when we win this trophy again.

Both lads knew, from their point of view,
they had seen all there was to win.
League Cup aside, they'd stood with pride,
knowing we were the best there'd been.
Bob thought "right", "we won't take it light",
and we'll win that trophy too.
At Villa Park, floodlit in the dark,
that's exactly what we do.

If you think that I'd let you see us,
win the cup by yourself, you're wrong.
I'm always there next to you,
when we sing our Liverpool song.
Our leader Bob is our hero,
we'll walk on through the wind and rain.
And side by side we'll be standing,
when we win this trophy again.

To '84, the man they adore,
has decided to call it a day.
Joe stepped in, as he was akin,
to the Liverpool winning way.
Paul and John's glee, as Joe won all three,
that first treble became folklore.
And they were there, punching the air,
as they'd always done before.

If you think that I'd let you see us,
win the cup by yourself, you're wrong.
I'm always there next to you,
when we sing our Liverpool song.
Our leader Joe is our hero,
we'll walk on through the wind and rain.
And side by side we'll be standing,
when we win this trophy again.

Dalglish came and things stayed the same,
with the best football side around.
Things went great, for Paul and his mate,
'til we played at the Hillsborough ground.
Policemen froze, a barrier goes,
and our fans are in awful strife.
John did his best, along with the rest,
but they couldn't save Paul's life.

If you think that I'd let you see us,
win the cup by yourself, you're wrong.
I am still stood right by you,
when you sing our Liverpool song.
I've got Shanks, Joe and Bob beside me,
we're all there away and home.
And all of Heaven is singing,
"You'll Never Walk Alone".

Underneath The Floodlights
(To the tune of German love song 'Lili Marlene')

Underneath the floodlights,
Down in Dusseldorf,
All the kop were singing,
Bevvied up of course.
We've been to Lisbon and to Rome,
And our team "never walk alone,"
We're going off to Europe to bring the cup back home.

All the way from Anfield to the gates of Rome,
All the way from Anfield to bring the trophy home.
Nothing can stop us come what may,
We'll have our say, this is our day,
Liverpool's red army,
Is marching on its way.

*(Based on the song 'Lili Marlene', this Kop song first emerged in the
late Seventies. The original song was based on a German poem from
1915 and soon became a favourite of both German and American
troops during the Second World War)*

Vladi Smicer
(To the 'Flintstones' theme tune)

Smicer, Vladi Smicer,
He's the greatest player in history.
From the Czech Republic,
He's about to score a goal for me.

We Are Liverpool (Tra La La La La)
(To the tune of Boney M's 'Brown Girl In The Ring')

[Chorus]:
We are Liverpool, tra la la la la,
We are Liverpool, tra la la la la la,
We are Liverpool, tra la la la la,
The best football team in the world – yes we are!

Poetry in motion, tra la la la la,
Poetry in motion, tra la la la la la,
Poetry in motion, tra la la la la,
The best football team in the world – yes we are!

If you want to know the score,
Listen to the Anfield roar,
If you face us on the park,
Our bite is worse than our bark – we're Liverpool!

If you see us playing there,
Sheer magic in the air,
When the big Red Army comes,
Better lay down your guns!

We are Liverpool, tra la la la la,
We are Liverpool, tra la la la la la,
We are Liverpool, tra la la la la,
The best football team in the world – yes we are!

Poetry in motion, tra la la la la,
Poetry in motion, tra la la la la la,
Poetry in motion, tra la la la la,
The best football team in the world – yes we are!

Went to Europe feeling good,
Played them how they knew we would,
Though they fear us going there,
We beat them fair and square.

One goal in the net, tra la la la la,
Two goals in the net, tra la la la la la,
Three goals in the net, tra la la la la,
The best football team in the world!

We Are The Pride Of All Europe

We are the pride of all Europe,
The cocks of the north,
We hate United and Cockneys of course,
We only drink whiskey,
And bottles of brown,
The Liverpool boys are in town.
Na na na na na na na na...

We Can Do It

Yeah, we can do it,
Yeah we can do it,
Yeah, yeah, yeah.

[Chorus]:
We can really move,
(Yeah, we can do it),
We can really move,
(Yeah, we can do it),
We can really move,
(Yeah, we can do it),
We can really move, we can do it,
we can do it.

We can really move,
(Yeah, we can do it),
We can really move,
(Yeah, we can do it),
We can really move,
(Yeah, we can do it),
We can really move, we can do it,
we can do it.

You remember '65?
We really had the place alive,
We had it all on our side,
We took 'em all for a ride.

Now we're back and we're here to stay,
We're really gonna take it all away,
We come along and this is it,
We can really do it, now we're back again.

We can do it, we can do it,
We can really move,
We're ahead right now and we just can't lose,
We really are good news.
We can do it, we can do it,
We can really move.

We can really move,
(Yeah, we can do it),
We can really move,
(Yeah, we can do it),
We can really move,
(Yeah, we can do it),
We can really move, we can do it,
we can do it.

We can really move,
(Yeah, we can do it),
We can really move,
(Yeah, we can do it),
We can really move,
(Yeah, we can do it),
We can really move, we can do it,
we can do it.

We really moving, we're havin' fun.
We got the others on the run,
It looks good and we feel the same,
What we done before we can do again.

We got it goin', we got it made,
We leave the others in the shade,
This time we're gonna show them how,
We can do it, we can do it, we can, do it now.

We can do it, we can do it,
We can really move,
We're ahead right now and we just can't lose,
We really are good news.
We can do it, we can do it,
We can, really move.

We can really move,
(Yeah, we can do it),
We can really move,
(Yeah, we can do it),
We can really move,
(Yeah, we can do it),
We can really move, we can do it,
we can do it.

[Guitar riff]

We can do it, we can do it,
We can really move,
We're ahead right now and we just can't lose,
We really are good news.
We can do it, we can do it,
We can really move.

We can do it, we can do it,
We can really move,
We're ahead right now and we just can't lose,
We got style and we can prove,
We can do it, we can do it,
We can really move.

(The official club anthem to the 1977 FA Cup final with
Manchester United, reaching number 15 in the UK charts)

We Love You Liverpool, We Do

Another regularly heard chant at Anfield, although only the chorus usually gets an airing. It's also fitting that it originates from a song about The Beatles entitled: 'We Love The Beatles, We Do' which was a 1964 hit for an American group.

We Love You Liverpool, We Do

[Chorus]:
We love you Liverpool, we do,
We love you Liverpool, we do,
We love you Liverpool, we do,
Oh Liverpool we love you.

Shankly is our hero, he showed us how to play,
The mighty Reds of Europe are out to win today.
He made a team of champions, with every man a king,
And every game we love to win, and this is what we sing:

We love you Liverpool, we do,
We love you Liverpool, we do,
We love you Liverpool, we do,
Oh Liverpool we love you.

Clemence is our goalie, the best there is around,
And Keegan is the greatest that Shankly ever found.
Heighway is our favourite, a wizard of the game,
And here's the mighty Toshack to do it once again.

We love you Liverpool, we do,
We love you Liverpool, we do,
We love you Liverpool, we do,
Oh Liverpool we love you.

We've won the league, we've won the cup,
We're masters of the game.
And just to prove how good we are,
We'll do it all again.
We've got another team to beat and so we've got to try,

'Cos we're the best in all the land,
And that's the reason why:

We love you Liverpool, we do,
We love you Liverpool, we do,
We love you Liverpool, we do,
Oh Liverpool we love you.

We Shall Not Be Moved

We shall not, we shall not be moved,
We shall not, we shall not be moved,
Just like a team, that's gonna win the European
Cup again!
We shall not be moved.

*(An old union protest song of American origins that was
reshaped by fans of Shankly's Championship-winning side
to a song of triumphant defiance with the original third line
being 'just like the team that's gonna win the Football
League again'. It became one of the regular chants as the
Kop sparked into tune during the '60s and has been copied
by more or less every set of supporters)*

We Three Kings
(To the tune of Christmas carol 'We Three Kings Of Orient Are')

We three cups of Liverpool are:
Worthington, FA and UEFA.
Thanks to Hyypia,
We will beat yer,
Travelling from afar.

We Won It Five Times

(To the tune of 'Sloop John B' by The Beach Boys)

We won it at Wem-ber-ly,
We won it in Gay Paree,
In '77 and '84 it was Rome.

[Chorus]:
We've won it five times,
We've won it five times,
In Istanbul, we won it five times.

When Emlyn lifted it high,
He lit up the Roman sky,
Thommo in Paris and Souness did it aswell.

We've won it five times,
We've won it five times,
In Istanbul, we won it five times.

At Wembley we won it our home,
Took 26,000 to Rome,
20,000 to Paris when we won it again.

We've won it five times,
We've won it five times,
In Istanbul, we won it five times.

Stevie G's eyes lit up,
As he lifted the European Cup,
21 years and now it's coming back home.

We've won it five times,
We've won it five times,
In Istanbul, we won it five times.

We'll Be Coming

(To the Tartan Army tune 'We'll Be Coming')

We'll be coming,
We'll be coming,
We'll be coming down the road,
When you hear the noise of the Billy Shankly boys,
We'll be coming down the road.

We'll Win It Five Times

(To the tune of 'Sloop John B' by The Beach Boys)

We won it at Wem-ber-ly,
We won it in Gay Paree,
In '77 and '84 it was Rome.

We've won it four times,
We've won it four times.
The Mancs won it twice,
But we've won it four times.

We've won it four times,
We've won it four times,
In Istanbul we'll win it five times.

Wembley's Our Second Home

(To the tune of 'In My Liverpool Home')

Wembley's our second home,
Wembley's our second home,

We're going to Wembley to cheer on our team,
To fight for the best team that we've ever seen,
And watch Emlyn Hughes get the cup off the Queen,
Wembley's our second home.

From our Liverpool home,
The Reds will go marching to Rome.
We'll give Moenchengladbach a night to forget,
As goal after goal flies into their net.
Borussia won't beat us 'cos we are the best,
The Reds will go marching to Rome.

We're A Happy Band

We sing our songs with joy and pride,
Every time we watch our side,
In all the league we are top,
We're members of the mighty Kop (mighty Kop).

Liverpool supporters we're a happy band, (Ee-aye-addio),
That's because we're following the best team in the land.

We're leaving in the morning light,
Flying on a chartered plane,
By noon we'll be in Budapest,
By nine we'll know which team is best,
(team is best).

Hungarians may laugh and grin,
But wait till Roger bangs one in,
And St John will make them frown,
We'll bring the iron curtain down,
(curtain down).

Their goulash may be up to scratch,
But that won't help them win the match,
When the winning goal brings down the house,
They'll all resort to eating Scouse (eating Scouse).

*(Travelling Reds prepare for the trip to the Hungarian capital
to face Honved in the third round of the Cup Winners' Cup in
1966 – a game which finished goalless, although the Reds
progressed to the semi-finals with a 2-0 second leg victory at
Anfield)*

We're Gonna Win The League

(To the tune 'For He's A Jolly Good Fellow)

We're gonna win the league,
We're gonna win the league,
And now your gonna believe us,
And now your gonna believe us,
And now your gonna believe us,
We're gonna win the league.

*(Now a traditional football chant, it was most common on the
Anfield terraces during the success-strewn days of the '60s
and '70s when Kopites would sing it from September
through to May)*

We're The Champions

Here in Liverpool we all say with pride,
We are the supporters of the greatest football side,
We are the champions, yes we are the kings,
We are the champions and that is why we sing:

[Chorus]:
Liverpool are the team,
We're the best you've ever seen,
You can stick United and the rest,
Liverpool are still the best,
Na na, na na na na, hey hey, we're the champions.

We have played the best in Europe and at home,
And our sportsmanship and skill to all is known,
We tie the champions, there can be no doubt,
We are the champions and that is why we shout:

Liverpool are the team,
We're the best you've ever seen,
You can stick United and the rest,
Liverpool are still the best,
Na na, na na na na, hey hey, we're the champions.

We thank all those teams that gave us such a fright,
Now as your champions we'll set the world alight,
We are the champions, shout it from the Kop,
We are the champions, that Liverpool are top.

Liverpool are the team,
We're the best you've ever seen,
You can stick United and the rest,
Liverpool are still the best,
Na na, na na na na, hey hey, we're the champions.

Liverpool are the team,
We're the best you've ever seen,
You can stick United and the rest,
Liverpool are still the best,
Na na, na na na na, hey hey, we're the champions.

We've Got A Big Pole In Our Goal

(To the tune of 'The Whole World In His Hands')

We've got a big Pole in our goal,
We've got a great big Pole in our goal,
We've got a big Pole in our goal,
We've got a big Pole in our goal.

(A song for Jerzy Dudek which got its best airing after his heroics in the 2005 Champions League final against AC Milan)

We've Got That Ronnie Whelan

(To the tune of 'You've Lost That Loving Feeling' by The Righteous Brothers)

We've got that Ronniieeeee Whelan,
Wooooah that Ronnie Whelan.

What A Waste Of Money

What a waste of money!

(Sarcastically sung to inspirational free transfer signing Gary McAllister after his last game for Liverpool in 2002)

When Liverpool Win The Cup

(To the tune of 'When Johnny Comes Marching Home')

While on the bus to Villa Park, haroo, haroo,
I heard my mate make this remark, haroo, haroo.

We made poor Chelsea weep and ill,
It's Liverpool 2 and Chelsea 0,
And we'll all get blind drunk when Liverpool win the cup.

So here's to Lawrence, Byrne, St John,
haroo, haroo,
Milne and Yeats and Stevenson,
haroo, haroo.
Hunt and Thompson, what a man,
Lawler, Smith and Callaghan,
And we'll all get blind drunk when Liverpool win the cup.

For the Liverpool lads raise your glass,
haroo, haroo.
To Stevenson who made the pass,
haroo, haroo.
Thompson had them in a trance,
Bonetti never stood a chance,
And we'll all get blind drunk when Liverpool win the cup.

It's Wembley on the first of May,
haroo, haroo,
It's Leeds United labour day,
haroo, haroo.
We'll be there to cheer Bill Shankly's side,
And bring the cup to Merseyside,
And we'll all get blind drunk when Liverpool win the cup.

And if it's a draw you'll hear us moan,
Let's use the coin that beat Cologne,
And we'll all get blind drunk when Liverpool win the cup.

(This song tells the story of the Reds' path to Wembley in 1965 and the promise of the club's first ever FA Cup, along with some liquid merriment. It is also the original song to the Torres chant)

Where Are The Lads?

*(To the tune of Irish Republican folk song
'The Boys Of The Old Brigade')*

Oh father why are you so sad,
Your face so pale and fraught,
When all us Reds are proud and glad,
Of the team that we support.
Oh son I see in memory's view,
Days of long ago you see,
When we cheered and sang,
And from the Kop there rang,
Songs of Liverpool FC.

[Chorus]:
Where are the lads who stood with me,
At Milan and Etienne?
Oh it grieves me that I will never see,
The Spion Kop again.

From Cantril Farm the call to arms,
Was heard by one and all,
And from Garston came brave young men,
To answer Shankly's call.
I think of them at St Etienne,
Who made the rafters shake,
And in '65, they brought the Kop alive,
And made poor Inter quake.

Where are the lads who stood with me,
At Milan and Etienne?
Oh it grieves me that I will never see,
The Spion Kop again.

And so my son I've told you why,
On this dark day I sigh,
As I recall great players all,
From the glory days gone by.
Who played before the greatest fans,
Their singing never stopped,
Oh they sang and cheered and Liverpool revered,
On the mighty Spion Kop.

Where are the lads who stood with me,
At Milan and Etienne?
Oh it grieves me that I will never see,
The Spion Kop again.

Who Do You Think You Are Kidding Mr Catterick?
(To the Dad's Army theme tune of
'Who Do You Think You Are Kidding Mr Hitler')

Who do you think you're kidding Harry Catterick,
If you think the 'Pools no good?
There's Stevie Heighway, John Toshack and Chrissy Lawler too,
They scored three goals for Liverpool
and worked it right up you!

So who do you think you are kidding Harry Catterick,
If you think the 'Pools no good?

The Kop was here, they came to cheer, a famous victory.
With Alan Evans, Tommy Smith,
And our leader Bill Shankly.
So who do you think you are kidding Harry Catterick,
If you think the 'Pools no good?

Well the Everton supporters they have
had quite just enough,
They'd seen their team two goals in front,
Then Shankly called his bluff, 1-2-3.

So who do you think you're kidding Harry Catterick,
If you think the 'Pools no good.

(Kopites remind then Everton boss Harry Catterick of the Reds'
3-2 derby victory at Anfield in November 1970)

Why Are We So Good?

(To the tune of Yorkshire folk song 'Ilkley Moor Baht 'At')

Oh why are we so GOOD?
Oh why are we so GOOD?
Oh why are we so GOOD?
Because we're Liverpool,
Because we're Liverpool,
Because we're Liverpool.

Win The European Cup For Me

(To the tune 'Save Your Love' by Renee & Renato)

Win the European Cup for me,
Wembley, Paris – twice in Italy.
In Istanbul we kept the cup,
Sixth time in Rome let's lift it up.
Win the European cup for me.
Na na na na na...

You'll Never Walk Alone

When you walk through a storm,
Hold your head up high,
And don't be afraid of the dark.
At the end of a storm,
There's a golden sky,
And the sweet silver song of the lark.

Walk on through the wind,
Walk on through the rain,
Though your dreams be tossed and blown.
Walk on, walk on, with hope in your heart,
And you'll never walk alone,
You'll never walk alone.

Walk on, walk on,
With hope in your heart,
And you'll never walk alone,
You'll never walk alone.

You'll Never Walk Alone

Written by Rogers and Hammerstein for the 1945 Broadway musical 'Carousel', Gerry Marsden and his Pacemakers performed the song in Liverpool clubs during the birth of Merseybeat. Released in October 1963, YNWA – or 'the Liverpool FC song' as the world knows it – was the Pacemakers' third consecutive number one and nowhere was it more popular than on the Kop, as fans sang along with the PA before matches. When it fell from the top spot, Kopites continued to sing it and YNWA has been played and sung at Anfield ever since. It captures the very essence and unity of the club and remains a source of comfort to those affected by the tragic events that have hit the club.

You're Supposed To Let Us Win

You're supposed to,
You're supposed to,
You're supposed to let us win…

*(Sung to Norwich City when they were leading 1-0
in the final game played in front of the standing
Spion Kop in 1994)*

66 It was the Liverpool supporters who played their part so magnificently. From the sound and noise of half-time you would never have known it was Liverpool who were three down in Europe's showpiece final and Jamie Carragher was quick to go over to the fans at the final whistle and thank their 12th man. I do not think you would find the fans of many clubs staying so vociferous in such trying circumstances 99

– Mark Lawrenson after the 2005 Champions League final

“ A football club isn't just made up of players, coaches and directors. More than anything else it's the supporters who make a club, and that perhaps is the ingredient which best distinguishes Liverpool Football Club from every other team. The supporters. Because if one thing has remained obvious to me after these few years, it's that with supporters like you, Liverpool Football Club will never walk alone ”

– Luis Garcia

66 All of us found it a bit of a shock that night. It was one of the most impressive atmospheres I've played in and credit to the Liverpool fans for that, especially the Kop. They made it a memorable night, something special **99**

– John Terry on the 2005 Champions League semi-final

Song Index

- Benitez
- Benny Is A Dancer
- Best Midfield In The World
- Big Ron Yeats
- Bill Shankly From Glenbuck
- Billy Liddell
- Billy The King
- Biscan In Our Club
- Bjornebye In My Gang
- Blame It On Traore
- Blaydon Races
- Bolo, Bolo Bolo
- Build A Cabinet

- Cheyrou
- Come On You Mighty Reds
- Corners Of Europe
- Crouch, Crouch

- David Ngog
- Daylight Come And I Wanna Go Home
- Did The Ball Go In?
- Didi Hamann
- Diouf, Diouf, Diouf
- Diouf Is On Fire
- Doo Wah Didi, Didi

- O Come All Ye Faithful
- Oh Campione
- Oh Kyrgiakos
- Oh Liverpool Bill
- Oh Ronny Ronny
- Oh Sami Sami
- Oh When The Reds Go Marching In
- Oh Yossi Yossi
- One Andy Carroll
- One-Nil Down, Two-One Up
- Our Mighty Emlyn
- Over The Hills And Far Away

- Pass And Move (It's The Liverpool Groove)
- Patrik Berger
- Pepe Reina!
- Phil Babb
- Poor Scouser Tommy
- Put Your Hands Up For Dirk Kuyt

- Rafa In Istanbul
- Rafa, Rafael
- Rafa's Got His Dirk Out
- Raul The Red
- Red And White Kop
- Reds Never Tire
- Ring Of Fire
- Robbie Fowler
- Robbie Keane
- Rockin' Around With Stevie G
- Roma
- Romeo And Juliet

W

- We Are Liverpool (Tra La La La La)
- We Are The Pride Of All Europe
- We Can Do It
- We Love You Liverpool, We Do
- We Shall Not Be Moved
- We Three Kings
- We Won It Five Time
- We'll Be Coming
- We'll Win It Five Times
- Wembley's Our Second Home
- We're A Happy Band
- We're Gonna Win The League
- We're The Champions
- We've Got A Big Pole In Our Goal
- We've Got That Ronnie Whelan
- What a Waste Of Money
- When Liverpool Win The Cup
- Where Are The Lads?
- Who Do You Think You Are Kidding Mr Catterick?
- Why Are We So Good?
- Win The European Cup For Me

Y

- You'll Never Walk Alone
- You're Supposed To Let Us Win

66 I'm just one of the people who stands on the kop. They think the same as I do, and I think the same as they do. It's a kind of marriage of people who like each other 99

– Bill Shankly

❝I am extremely happy when I hear that fans of such a big team are singing my name. It's hard to describe my feelings at that moment. It's very encouraging for any footballer and one of the best things you can experience **❞**

– Sotirios Kyrgiakos

66The fans are fantastic. People say how good the Portsmouth fans are, and they are, but Liverpool fans are in a league of their own. When you walk out (at Anfield) and hear the fans singing the anthem, it helps. Every player is so proud to put on the shirt 99

– Glen Johnson

❝ I've heard about the song but I never actually heard it sung during a game and whenever I met Liverpool fans out and about, they were always complimentary. I think the chant was more of a media thing. I know people always look for a scapegoat in the team and that was me. I was criticised a lot during my time at Liverpool but mentally I'm quite strong ❞

– Djimi Traore on his Blame It On Traore song

❝I will never forget today and I want to thank all the fans who gave me such a great ovation. They were immense. I thought I would get a decent reception but that surpassed all my wildest dreams. That sort of ovation is normally reserved for players who have won European Cups for a club. It was a brilliant day and it was nice to hear the Kop's humour at its best again when they were telling me to go back to Coventry **❞**

– Gary McAllister after his last game for Liverpool at Anfield

66 On a European Cup night, there's nowhere like Anfield. When they sing 'You'll Never Walk Alone' it makes the hairs stand up on the back of your neck. They will drive their team on **99**

– Harry Redknapp

66 Liverpool's fans are just amazing. The best feeling I have at away games is Anfield. It is just incredible. I love it. You get goose bumps when you see their supporters sing You'll Never Walk Alone 99

– Thierry Henry

Other great Liverpool FC publications from £3.99

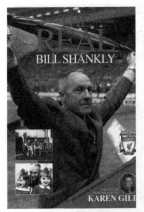
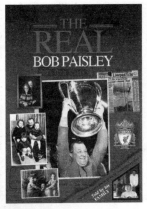
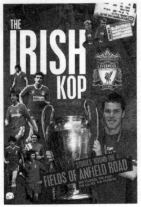

66 I used to stand on the Kop when I was here in 1969. The atmosphere and passion on the pitch as well as the terraces was intoxicating and Liverpool became part of me from that day on 99

– Gerard Houllier

THE ANFIELD SONGBOOK

WE HAVE DREAMS AND SONGS TO SING